Second Edition Revised

ECONOMICS
NEW WAYS OF THINKING

Applying the Principles Workbook

SCOTT WOLLA

EMC Publishing®

ST. PAUL, MINNESOTA

Publisher: Alex Vargas
Managing Editor: Brenda Owens
Production Manager: Bob Dreas
Cover Designer: Leslie Anderson
Design and Production Specialist: Tammy Norstrem

Care has been taken to verify the accuracy of information presented in this book. However, the authors, editors, and publisher cannot accept responsibility for Web, email, newsgroup subject matter or content, or for consequences from application of the information in this book, and make no warranty, expressed or implied, with respect to its content.

Trademarks: Some of the product names and company names included in this book have been used for identification purposes only and may be trademarks or registered trade names of their respective manufacturers and sellers. The authors, editors, and publisher disclaim any affiliation, association, or connection with, or sponsorship or endorsement by, such owners.

We have made every effort to trace the ownership of all copyrighted material and to secure permission from copyright holders. In the event of any question arising as to the use of any material, we will be pleased to make the necessary corrections in future printings. Thanks are due to the aforementioned authors, publishers, and agents for permission to use the materials indicated.

ISBN 978-1-53383-491-1

© by EMC Publishing, LLC
875 Montreal Way
St. Paul, MN 55102
Email: educate@emcp.com
Website: www.emcschool.com

Printed in the United States of America

27 26 25 24 23 22 21 20 19 18   1 2 3 4 5 6 7 8 9 10

CONTENTS

UNIT IV Macroeconomics

Unit V Trade and Investment

PREFACE

A good curriculum uses an excellent textbook as a foundation and a springboard for further learning. I have had the opportunity to read many textbooks in my teaching career, and I have found *Economics: New Ways of Thinking* superior in presenting complex economics issues in a clear, precise way. It goes beyond a simple listing of terms and concepts, and moves to something that is readable and engaging. It was to my benefit that I started with such a wonderful textbook in the writing of this workbook.

The study of economics is at its best when you are an active participant. It was from that belief that I wrote this *Applying the Principles Workbook*. In creating this book, I attempted to provide a bit of the actual experience of economics and to tie that experience to the textbook as closely as possible. The lessons attempt to push you beyond the stage of vocabulary retention to a level at which you are interacting with the content.

Scott Wolla

About the Author

Scott Wolla is senior economic education specialist at the Federal Reserve Bank of Saint Louis. Before his work with the Federal Reserve, Scott taught economics and history at Hibbing High School in Hibbing, Minnesota, for thirteen years.

Scott received his Bachelor of Science in social studies education from Minnesota State University Moorhead, Master of Science in education from Bemidji State University, and Master of Arts in economics for educators from the University of Delaware.

Scott was named High School Teacher of the Year by the Minnesota Council for the Social Studies (2006) and was awarded the Economic Educator Excellence Award (2006) and Innovative Economic Educator Award (2003) by the Minnesota Council on Economic Education.

Acknowledgments

I would like to thank EMC Publishing for offering me the opportunity to write this workbook, and Roger A. Arnold, author of the student textbook, for reviewing the workbook material and ensuring that it aligns with the textbook content.

Dedication

To my wife, Dawn, for her support and encouragement.

Name: _____   Date: _____

CHAPTER 1, SECTION 1

Scarcity

Guns or Butter

Economists often speak of the way a society chooses to allocate its resources toward the production of military goods or consumer goods as a "guns or butter" decision. Of course, guns represent resources allocated to a nation's defense; butter represents resources allocated for consumer goods. Economists use the phrase "guns *or* butter" because scarcity mandates that we choose how to use available resources.

Knowing how to understand and evaluate economic data presented in graphs, maps, charts, and tables is an important skill. Labels, titles, legends, and/or keys will assist you as you "read" the data and transfer information from one form to another (written to visual and vice versa).

Illustrate the relationship between guns and butter as directed in question 1.

1. Use the following data to draw a production possibilities frontier (PPF) on the grid shown.

Guns	Butter
0	15
3	14
8	11
11	7
12	4
13	0

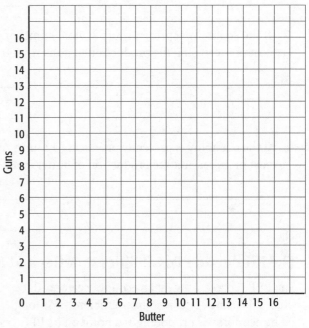

An Economy's Production Possibilities Frontier for Guns and Butter

Use the graph you created in question 1 to answer questions 2–8.

2. Can this economy produce 6 units of guns and 12 units of butter? Explain.

   _____

   _____

3. Can this economy produce 11 units of guns and 11 units of butter? Explain.

   _____

   _____

4. What does this PPF represent?

_____

_____

5. How does this PPF illustrate the concept of scarcity?

_____

_____

_____

6. How does this PPF illustrate the concept of opportunity cost?

_____

_____

_____

7. If the economy is presently producing 0 units of guns and 15 units of butter, what is the opportunity cost of increasing the production of guns from 0 units to 3 units?

_____

_____

8. If the economy is presently producing 12 units of guns and 4 units of butter, what is the opportunity cost of increasing the production of butter from 4 units to 11 units?

_____

_____

The Production Possibilities Frontier and Efficiency

The PPF represents what an economy can produce when it is using all its resources efficiently. As long as the economy is producing at a point on its PPF, it is producing at an **efficient** level and using all its resources.

When an economy is already using all its resources efficiently, it cannot use the same resources to produce something beyond, or outside, its PPF. Therefore, economists say that a point outside an economy's PPF is **unattainable.**

An economy _can_ produce at a point inside its PPF. However, if an economy is producing at a point inside its PPF, then either the economy is not using all its resources or it is using them inefficiently. Economists label a point inside the PPF **underutilization** because such a point indicates that the economy is underutilizing its resources.

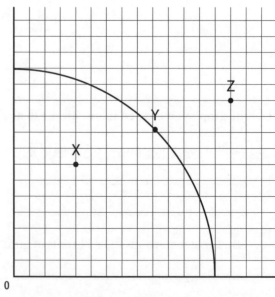

The PPF and Efficiency

Efficiency, unattainability, and underutilization are shown on the PPF and Efficiency graph on the previous page. Use the graph to answer questions 9–11.

9. The point that represents an unattainable point is _____.

10. The point that represents underutilization is _____.

11. An economy that is using all its resources efficiently is producing at point _____.

Shifts in the Production Possibilities Frontier

The PPF is determined by the level of economic resources. If the level of resources increases, the PPF will shift to the right and more goods and services can be produced. If the level of resources decreases, the PPF will shift to the left, which means the economy can no longer produce at previous levels. Because technological progress will enable an economy to produce more with the same resources, advancements in technology will result in a rightward shift of the PPF.

Write your answers to questions 12 and 13 on the lines provided.

12. What two things would cause the PPF of an economy to shift to the right (outward)?

_____

_____

13. What would cause the PPF of an economy to shift to the left (inward)?

_____

_____

Use the shifts in the PPF graph to answer questions 14–19. Assume that the PPF begins at the location labeled C. Read question 14 and determine the direction (left or right) that the PPF will move from location C in response to the event described. Then write the letter of the new location. Now read question 15 and determine the direction the PPF will move from the location you decided on in question 14. Then write the letter of the new location. Continue to determine the direction and location for each subsequent event.

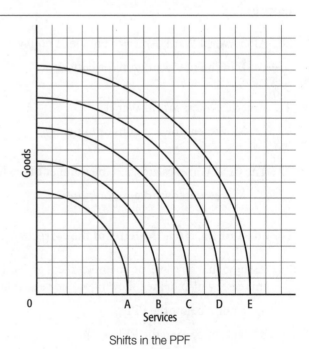

Shifts in the PPF

14. The invention of the lightbulb allows laborers to work later hours and introduces the midnight shift.

Direction: _____ Location: _____

15. A major drought makes much of America's farmland unproductive.

Direction: _____ Location: _____

16. The baby boomer generation starts to retire, and millions leave the workforce.

Direction: _____ Location: _____

17. The invention of the Internet allows people to communicate, do research, and conduct business from remote locations.

Direction: _____ Location: _____

18. The U.S. government loosens immigration requirements, allowing millions of skilled workers to enter the country.

Direction: _____ Location: _____

19. The invention of the cell phone allows people to communicate while commuting or from remote locations.

Direction: _____ Location: _____

A society makes choices that determine how it will allocate its resources between guns and butter. For each of the events in questions 20–23, circle either *guns* or *butter* to indicate whether the event would cause movement along the PPF toward producing more guns or toward producing more butter.

20. After World War I, America pursues a policy of "return to normalcy" and defense spending is cut.

Movement toward guns or butter?

21. America enters World War II.

Movement toward guns or butter?

22. The Cold War escalates and the number of nuclear warheads increases.

Movement toward guns or butter?

For question 23, circle the letter of the correct answer.

23. Assume that any level of unemployment above 4 percent represents underutilized (labor) resources. In this case, which of the following would represent an unemployment rate of 6 percent?

   a. a point below the PPF

   b. a point beyond the PPF

   c. a shift of the PPF to the right

   d. a shift of the PPF to the left

CHAPTER 1, SECTION 2

Incentives

> Most of economics can be summarized in four words: People respond to incentives.
>
> —Steven Landsburg, economist

Governments use economic incentives to influence the behavior of citizens in a way that benefits society. They create incentives through laws and through taxes.

For example, a government could pass a **law** prohibiting children from purchasing a product meant for use by adults. Such a law would make it difficult for children to obtain the product.

A government could also place a **tax** on a certain good that discourages its use. Such a tax would increase the price of the good. For some people, the higher price would decrease their consumption of the good.

A government could give **tax benefits** to encourage an activity. For example, it might provide a **credit** by giving taxpayers back a portion of a tax, or it might provide a **deduction** by allowing taxpayers to subtract a certain amount from their income before calculating their taxes. In terms of cost-benefit analysis, such a credit or deduction would reduce the cost of the activity. For some people, the benefit will then be greater than the cost, and these people would increase their participation in the activity.

For each of the goals in questions 1–6, think of a government incentive that accomplishes the goal.

EXAMPLE

Goal: Decrease the consumption of alcohol.

Incentive:

_____

_____

_____

1. *Goal:* Decrease smoking.

   Incentive:

   _____

   _____

   _____

2. *Goal:* Increase the level of education.

   Incentive:

   _____

   _____

3. *Goal:* Increase the rate of private home ownership.

   Incentive:

   _____

   _____

   _____

4. *Goal:* Decrease the consumption of fuel oil.

   Incentive:

   _____

   _____

   _____

5. *Goal:* Increase the rate of personal savings.

   Incentive:

   _____

   _____

6. *Goal:* Increase donations to charities.

   Incentive:

   _____

   _____

For questions 7 and 8, write two goals (other than those mentioned in questions 1–6) that you think would benefit society, and describe an incentive that will accomplish each goal.

7. *Goal:*

   _____

   _____

   Incentive:

   _____

   _____

8. *Goal:*

   _____

   _____

   Incentive:

   _____

Refer to the goals and incentives in questions 1–6 as you answer questions 9 and 10.

9. What is the trade-off of using tax benefits as incentives?

_____

_____

10. Could any of these incentives have unintended effects? Explain.

_____

_____

_____

Economists assume that people are rational beings who weigh the costs and benefits of various options before making a decision. In short, they view human behavior as a response to incentives.

Suppose absenteeism is a problem in your school. In questions 11–17, your task is to analyze the present costs and benefits of attending school, come up with an incentive system that will improve attendance at your school, and analyze that system.

11. What are the present costs?

    Costs of attending school:

    _____

    ._____

12. What are the present benefits?

    Benefits of attending school:

    _____

13. In creating your incentive plan, you can (1) decrease the costs of attending school, (2) increase the benefits of attending school, or both. Write your incentive plan below.

    _____

    _____

    _____

    _____

    _____

    _____

    _____

    _____

14. How will your incentive plan increase student attendance?

_____

_____

_____

15. Is your plan practical and feasible? Explain.

_____

_____

_____

16. What are the trade-offs to using these incentives?

_____

_____

_____

17. Could any of these incentives have unintended effects? Explain.

_____

_____

_____

Apply what you have learned in this section by completing the following extension activities.

18. Present a Career Path Think of a career that interests you. Using multiple sources, research the estimated total cost of embarking on that career. Include the cost of any education, training, licenses, and capital (such as computers or tools). Then research the average income earned by a beginner in the field. Using formal English, prepare and deliver a presentation in which you present the investment required to enter the career and the incentive to do so—that is, the expected income.

   After you have made your presentation to the class, ask whether anyone has questions about your topic. If so, either answer the questions or complete additional research to find the answers. As your classmates deliver their presentations, listen carefully and ask questions as needed to clarify your understanding of the costs and benefits of their chosen professions.

19. Explain in Your Own Words Consider the "Your Personal Economics" feature in your textbook and research economic inflation and the economic theories that explain it. Use at least two sources of information and take careful notes during your research. Then, write a paragraph explaining in your own words what inflation is and what causes it. Review your paragraph for correct spelling, subject-verb agreement, pronoun agreement, and verb tenses. Make corrections as needed.

Name: _____ Date: _____

CHAPTER 1, SECTION 3

Resources

Use the following key to label each of the resources in questions 1–16 as land, labor, capital, or entrepreneurship. If a resource is land, identify it as either renewable or nonrenewable. If a resource is a capital good, identify it as either physical or human. (*Hint:* Physical capital is a tangible, human-made resource—such as tools or machinery—used to produce other goods and services.

> Ld-r = land (renewable)
> Ld-n = land (nonrenewable)
> Lbr = labor
> C = capital
> E = entrepreneurship

1. coal _____

2. telephone _____

3. natural gas _____

4. computer _____

5. truck driver _____

6. accountant _____

7. forklift _____

8. oak trees _____

9. corn _____

10. computer programmer _____

11. Bill Gates _____

12. cotton _____

13. gold _____

14. hammer _____

15. Henry Ford _____

16. lawyer _____

Look at your desk at school or at home. For each of the categories identified in questions 17–20, determine the resources that were used to produce the desk.

17. land

_____

18. labor

_____

19. capital

_____

20. entrepreneurship

_____

_____

Write your answer to question 21 on the lines provided.

21. As a student at school, which (if any) of the four economic resources are you? Defend your answer.

_____

_____

_____

_____

Apply what you have learned in this section by completing the following extension activity.

22. Collaborate on a Business Plan Working with a group of classmates, brainstorm ideas for new businesses you believe would be successful. As a group, choose one business idea and work together to write a business plan. Include the name of the business, a description of the good or service it provides, and all the capital and business property, such as vehicles, office space, computers, and tools, that you will need for your business.

   Assign roles and present your business plan to the class as a group. When all business plans have been presented, the class will vote on which business has the best chance of succeeding based on the information provided.

23. Discuss a Failed Business Plan Using the original business plan you and your group created in the activity above, imagine that your business plan failed. Examine the capital that your business owns and discuss how you will dispose of your business property. Can anything be returned, sold, or used in a different way? Once you have decided how to dispose of your capital, present your plans to the rest of the class and decide, as a group, which business was the most successful at reusing or recouping the costs of their business property.

CHAPTER 2, SECTION 1

Economic Systems

Three Economic Questions

The ability to summarize information is a necessary skill. A *summary* is a shortened version of something that has been said or written, stating its main point(s). When you summarize something, you typically restate the concept in your own words. In questions 1–3, state the three economic questions that all nations must answer, and summarize what each question means.

1. *Economic question:*

   _____

   Summary of economic question:

   _____

   _____

2. *Economic question:*

   _____

   Summary of economic question:

   _____

   _____

3. *Economic question:*

   _____

   Summary of economic question:

   _____

   _____

   _____

Comparing Free Enterprise and Socialism

Write your answers to questions 4–7 on the lines provided.

4. What is free enterprise?

   _____

   _____

5. Today, the United States is often described as having a free enterprise economic system. What other terms do economists use to refer to a *free enterprise* system? (i.e., What terms are synonymous with free enterprise?)

_____

6. What is socialism?

_____

_____

7. What two terms are confused with *socialism* but actually refer to types of socialism?

_____

Answer question 8 by completing the table provided.

8. Comparing information is often easier when the information is organized in a table. Complete the following table to compare free enterprise and socialism in six major areas.

Area	Free enterprise	Socialism
Resources		
Government's role in the economy		
Economic plans		
Income distribution		
Controlling prices		
Private property		

Mixed Economies

Write your answers to questions 9 and 10 on the lines provided.

9. What is a mixed economy?

_____

_____

Applying the Principles Workbook

10. Why is a mixed economy not considered a major economic system along with free enterprise and socialism?

_____

_____

_____

The United States' Mixed Economy

The U.S. economy, which is a mixed economy, includes elements of both free enterprise and socialism. Write your answers to questions 11 and 12 on the lines provided.

11. What elements of free enterprise does the U.S. economy include?

_____

_____

12. What elements of socialism does the U.S. economy include?

_____

_____

Apply what you have learned in this section by completing the following extension activities.

13. **Examine Economic Freedom** Exhibit 2-1 in the text identified the economic freedom scores for various countries. The full list of countries can be found at http://econ.emcp.net/econfreedom. Pick three countries from three different sections of the list and research what it is that makes the country economically free or unfree. Investigate the average or median income of the people in each country, the standard of living (as measured by GDP per capita), and so on. Write an analysis of your findings and share a summary with your class.

14. **Research Incentives** Research and identify the countries in the world today that impose price controls on various goods (examine current socialist economic systems). Search to see if producers are freely producing and supplying those goods and how these controls may be affecting incentives compared to countries that do not impose price controls. The incentive to produce is closely tied to whether or not private property exists and to whether or not prices are free to reflect the demands of the buying public. After your investigation, write a two- to three-paragraph summary of your findings.

15. **Describe Differences within Economic Systems** In a compare-and-contrast essay, describe the differences between economic systems. Focus your comparisons on competition and incentives within free enterprise and socialism.

CHAPTER 2, SECTION 1

The Visions

Answer question 1 by completing the table.

1. Complete the following table by identifying some of the differences between Adam Smith and Karl Marx.

Topic	Adam Smith	Karl Marx
Place and year of birth		
Education		
Major work		
Vision		

In questions 2–5, use the information from Exhibit 2-2 to briefly describe the views of Adam Smith on the topics listed.

2. self-interest

_____

_____

3. division of labor

_____

_____

4. competition

_____

_____

5. government

_____

_____

In questions 6–8, use the information from Exhibit 2-2 to briefly describe the views of Karl Marx on the topics listed.

6. value of produced goods

_____

_____

7. capitalists

_____

_____

8. development of nations

_____

_____

Use the following key to label each of the statements in questions 9–18 as more like the free enterprise vision of Adam Smith or as more like the socialist vision of Karl Marx.

S = Adam Smith, free enterprise vision
M = Karl Marx, socialist vision

9. _____ Resources should be owned by private individuals.

10. _____ Government decision makers should write economic plans.

11. _____ Private property should be sacred.

12. _____ Government should make major decisions concerning the use of resources and the production of goods.

13. _____ Much attention should be given to distribute income away from high earners toward low earners.

14. _____ Government should own and control many resources.

15. _____ Government should not attempt to control prices.

16. _____ Government should only play a small role in the economy.

17. _____ Government should set wages and the prices of goods.

18. _____ Government should own most property and use it for the benefit of the people.

Apply what you have learned in this section by completing the following extension activities.

19. **Collaborate on a Debate** Participate in a classroom debate between socialist and free enterprise economic ideas of the proper role of government in the economy. One half of the class will debate in favor of socialism, while the other half will debate in favor of capitalism. Work with your group to discuss the benefits and limitations of your assigned subject and help prepare notes for the debate. Consider such questions as: should the government play a large role or small role? What are the costs and benefits of government regulation and income redistribution? Make sure your group addresses your economic system's effect on fairness, freedom, and standard of living.

    When your notes are complete, choose a teammate to debate on behalf of the group. The debaters representing each group should take turns speaking about each of the points: fairness, freedom, and standard of living. Group members should be encouraged to assist in the debate by sharing information and helping their selected speaker remember key details.

20. **Find the Main Idea** Knowing how to identify the main idea in an article or presentation is a valuable skill. The main idea is a brief statement of what you think the author wants you to know, think, or feel after reading the text (or hearing the speech). In some cases, the main idea is clearly stated. Use the Internet to find an article on economics or economic theory that has not been discussed in your textbook. Print out the article (or a transcript of the speech) and try to identify the main idea. Once you have determined the main idea, write the main idea at the top of the page. Next, go through the article and underline the important details that support the main idea. Finally, identify whether you agree or disagree with the article and explain why or why not.

21. **Compare Economic Systems** Continue the discussion on the differences between socialist and free enterprise economies by comparing two characteristics of economic systems: incentives and competition. In a compare-and-contrast essay, describe the differences between competition and incentives within these different economic systems.

22. **Research Visionaries** From this chapter it is clear that economic philosophers from days past have an impact on the economic systems of today. Research the work of Adam Smith, Friedrich Hayek, Milton Friedman, and John Maynard Keynes and analyze the importance of their work and the impact it has on the U.S. free enterprise system. Use your analysis to identify which elements of their work exist in today's free enterprise system. Cite the sources that you use and then transfer your written research into a new medium (such as a PowerPoint presentation, Excel document, or audio recording).

Name: _____ Date: _____

CHAPTER 2, SECTION 2

Globalization

Evidence of the Movement Toward Globalization

Certain facts provide evidence that globalization is happening. In questions 1–6, use the information in Exhibit 2-3 to describe how the facts listed indicate the trend toward globalization.

1. decline in U.S. tariff rates

_____

_____

2. increase in foreign exchange trading

_____

_____

3. increase in foreign direct investment

_____

_____

4. increase in U.S. personal foreign investment

_____

_____

5. increase in membership in the World Trade Organization (WTO)

_____

_____

6. easier worldwide communication

_____

_____

_____

Causes of the Movement Toward Globalization

In questions 7–9, explain how each of the factors listed has led to the recent period of globalization.

7. the end of the Cold War

   _____

   _____

   _____

8. advancing technology

   _____

   _____

   _____

9. policy changes

   _____

   _____

   _____

Benefits of Globalization

In questions 10 and 11, list the major benefits put forth by those who favor globalization. Then describe how each is a good thing. Write your answers on the lines provided.

10. *Benefit:*

    _____

    Description:

    _____

    _____

    _____

11. *Benefit:*

    _____

    Description:

    _____

    _____

    _____

    _____

Costs of Globalization

In questions 12–14, list and describe the major costs put forth by the critics of globalization. Then summarize the response that supporters of globalization might offer for each cost. Write your answers on the lines provided.

12. *Cost:*

_____

Description:

_____

_____

_____

Response:

_____

13. *Cost:*

_____

Description:

_____

_____

_____

Response:

_____

_____

_____

14. *Cost:*

_____

Description:

_____

_____

_____

Response:

_____

_____

_____

Debating Globalization

Write your answers to questions 15 and 16 on the lines provided.

15. Do you think Adam Smith or Karl Marx would be more supportive of globalization? Explain.

_____

_____

_____

16. Examine the arguments of the critics and the supporters of globalization. Do you agree with the critics or the supporters? Would you like to see more or less globalization in the future? How will globalization affect you personally? How will globalization affect your local economy? Write a letter to the editor of the _Wall Street Journal_ or to your local paper, expressing your ideas and arguments about globalization.

_____

_____

_____

_____

_____

_____

_____

Apply what you have learned in this section by completing the following extension activities.

17. **Make Your Case to a CEO** Imagine that you live in the small city of Centerville, which has a solid economy and a low unemployment rate. One of Centerville's main employers is Clover Computers. The CEO of Clover Computers, Cindy Chavez, has said that she plans to offshore 70% of the company's jobs in the next year because of the high cost of labor in the U.S. She claims that if she didn't offshore jobs, the company would have to downsize and cut the number and variety of computers they produce.

    Write a letter to Cindy Chavez either supporting or opposing the decision to offshore jobs. Describe specific possible benefits and drawbacks for individuals, the city itself, and the U.S. Be sure to use appropriate connecting words such as _because_ and _therefore_. Review your letter for correct spelling, subject-verb agreement, pronoun agreement, and verb tenses. Make corrections as needed.

_____

_____

_____

_____

_____

_____

How might your response differ depending on whether you were an employee of Clover Computers or a consumer of Clover Computers?

_____

_____

_____

_____

18. **Present a Country's Customs and Traditions** Choose one of the more globalized countries from Exhibit 2-4 in your book (those in the purple section). Research the customs and traditions that Americans would need to know in order to do business effectively in that country, including how to greet people respectfully in the language of that country. Then prepare a short presentation for the class describing how to behave in a business environment in the country you have researched. Practice your presentation by reading it aloud into a tape recorder or in front of a classmate. If you are unsure of the pronunciation of any words, look up the pronunciations and write them down phonetically (how they sound).

While your classmates make their presentations, listen carefully, take notes, and ask questions as needed to clarify your understanding of the country's cultural expectations.

After all the presentations have been completed, your teacher will assign each student a country. Students from different countries will pair off, and each student will greet his or her partner in a manner appropriate for the assigned country.

19. **Evaluate Data Using Maps**
Evaluate the following economic data on trading relationships by interpreting the map and transferring the information into a written summary. Your summary should identify exactly what information is being conveyed in the map.

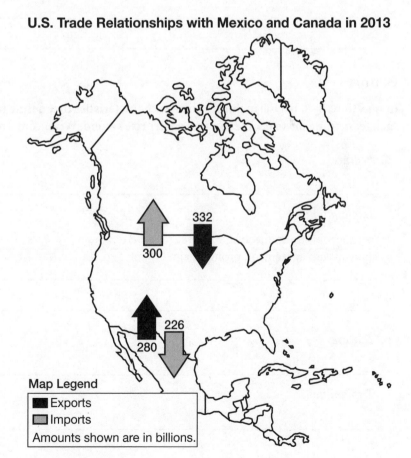

U.S. Trade Relationships with Mexico and Canada in 2013

332
300
226
280

Map Legend
■ Exports
▨ Imports
Amounts shown are in billions.

CHAPTER 3, SECTION 1
Characteristics of Free Enterprise

Three Economic Questions

In questions 1–3, explain how free enterprise answers the three economic questions all nations must decide how to answer.

1. What goods will be produced?

   _____

   _____

2. How will the goods be produced?

   _____

   _____

3. For whom will the goods be produced?

   _____

   _____

Features

In questions 4–8, list the major features or characteristics that define free enterprise. Then explain what each feature means to people in a free enterprise system. Write your answers in the blanks provided.

4. *Feature:*

   _____

   Explanation:

   _____

   _____

   _____

5. *Feature:*

   _____

   Explanation:

   _____

   _____

   _____

6. *Feature:*

_____

Explanation:

_____

_____

_____

7. *Feature:*

_____

Explanation:

_____

_____

_____

8. *Feature:*

_____

Explanation:

_____

_____

_____

Write your answers to questions 9 and 10 in the spaces provided.

9. How do legal systems and institutions either help or hinder free enterprise?

_____

_____

_____

10. Explain the role of economic incentives in your life. What economic incentives do you react to every day? For example, what economic incentives motivate you to go to school and to drive the speed limit?

_____

_____

_____

_____

Circular Flow

The following diagram shows the economic relationships that exist between different the U.S. economy. Use the diagram to answer questions 11–16.

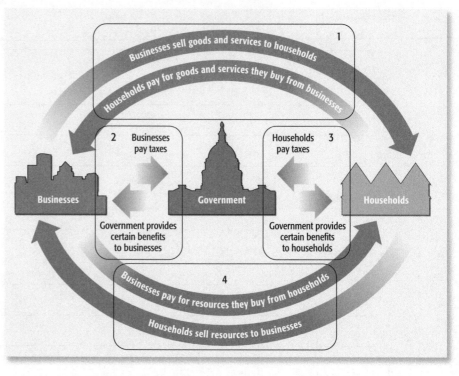

The Circular Flow of Economic Activity in the U.S. Economy

11. What economic activities flow from businesses to households?

_____

_____

12. What economic activities flow from households to businesses?

_____

_____

13. What economic activities flow from government to households?

_____

14. What economic activities flow from households to government?

_____

15. What economic activities flow from government to businesses and businesses to government?

_____

16. How is the circular flow model affected by the rest of the world? Explain your answer.

_____

_____

_____

In questions 17–25, identify the part of the circular flow diagram in which the economic activity listed occurs. Write 1, 2, 3, or 4 in the blanks provided.

17. _____ Mycah attends a public school.

18. _____ Travis buys a new car.

19. _____ Mikayla works 20 hours a week at Burger Barn.

20. _____ Rachel does research at a large corporation.

21. _____ Microsoft relies on the Justice Department to enforce copyright and patent laws.

22. _____ Dianne drives on County Road 1 to get to work.

23. _____ Bruce leases his commercial building to Widgets, Inc.

24. _____ Dawn buys a computer from her local office supply store.

25. _____ Vanh buys a lawn mower from Home Depot.

Questions 26–28 relate to the flow of resources in the circular flow diagram. Write your answers on the lines provided.

26. If a recession causes households to reduce spending, how might businesses be affected?

_____

_____

27. If government raises taxes on businesses, how might households be affected?

_____

28. If government cuts taxes on households, how might businesses be affected?

_____

Draw a circular flow model in the space below that displays this change.

CHAPTER 3, SECTION 2

Profit and Loss in Free Enterprise

Complete the formulas in questions 1–4.

1. Total revenue = _____.

2. Total cost = _____.

3. Profit = _____.

4. Loss = _____.

Bryan sells gadgets at a price of $7 apiece. His average cost is $5 per gadget. On Monday, Bryan sold 10 gadgets; on Tuesday, he sold 7 gadgets; on Wednesday, he sold 9 gadgets; on Thursday, he sold 11 gadgets; and on Friday, he sold 13 gadgets.

Write your answers to questions 5–8 in the blanks provided.

5. What was Bryan's total revenue for the week? _____

6. What was Bryan's total cost for the week? _____

7. Did Bryan have a profit or a loss for the week? _____

8. What was the dollar amount of Bryan's profit or loss for the week? _____

Write your answers to questions 9 and 10 in the blanks provided.

9. You have likely heard someone say, "Every time I turn on the TV, all I see are reality shows, and every time I turn on the radio, all I hear is pop music. Why do TV networks and radio stations all broadcast the same content? Why can't they be original for a change?" What could you say about profit and loss as signals to someone who says this?

   _____

   _____

   _____

   _____

   _____

   _____

10. If some automobile companies are earning large profits from the manufacture and sale of hybrid cars, what do economists predict will be the response of other auto manufacturers?

_____

_____

_____

_____

_____

CHAPTER 3, SECTION 3

The Ethics of Free Enterprise

An Ethical System

Just as ethics—the principles of conduct, such as right and wrong, morality and immorality, good and bad—applies to the behavior of individuals, ethics applies to the behavior of an economic system. In questions 1–4, list and describe the goals that free enterprise needs to meet in order to be considered an ethical economic system.

1. *Goal:*

   _____

   Description:

   _____

   _____

2. *Goal:*

   _____

   Description:

   _____

   _____

3. *Goal:*

   _____

   Description:

   _____

   _____

4. *Goal:*

   _____

   Description:

   _____

Government Subsidies

One role of government is to keep the country's economic system running smoothly. If most citizens have jobs, people are generally happier with government's role. In some cases, the government might subsidize failing or struggling businesses in order to save jobs. Write your answers to questions 5 and 6 in the blanks provided.

5. What might be the reason why a business is failing?

_____

_____

_____

_____

6. Why might people consider it to be unethical to save a failing business?

_____

_____

_____

_____

Key Documents

In questions 7–9, identify the feature of free enterprise (private property, choice, or competition) contained in the document listed. Then describe the document's reference to the feature. Write your answers in the blanks provided.

7. Bill of Rights

Feature:

_____

Description:

_____

_____

8. Declaration of Independence

Feature:

_____

Description:

_____

_____

9. U.S. Constitution

Feature:

_____

Description:

_____

_____

Rights and Responsibilities

Write your answer to question 10 on the lines provided.

10. People in a free enterprise economy have certain rights, but they also have responsibilities. What are people's responsibilities in a free enterprise economy?

_____

_____

_____

_____

Apply what you have learned in this section by completing the following extension activities.

11. Collaborate on a Movie Working with a partner or a small group of classmates, imagine that you are executives at a major movie studio. You want to make a new blockbuster movie—one that makes record-breaking profits. Keeping the idea of profit and loss as signals in mind, collaborate to research the highest-paid actors and highest-grossing films of the last two years. Take notes on your findings and then share ideas and opinions to plan your blockbuster.

Use your research to help you decide what the movie will be about, what it will be called, who the lead actors will be, and what tagline should accompany the title of the film. Work together to design and create a poster for your movie. Finally, present your business plan to your classmates, including the details of the film and your strategy to make it profitable.

12. Present Your Opinion Research the auto industry crisis of 2008–2010. Read at least two articles from reputable sources and take notes on the economic situation at the time, the government's response, and the results for Ford, GM, and Chrysler. Then decide whether you think the government's bailout of the auto industry was a good or bad idea and why.

Partner with a classmate and take turns responding to what you read by presenting your opinions. Be sure to explain why you think as you do. When you have finished presenting, take questions from your partner and answer them thoughtfully. Your partner will then summarize your position. While your partner is presenting, monitor your comprehension to make sure you understand his or her position. Ask questions as needed to clarify your understanding and then summarize your partner's position.

CHAPTER 3, SECTION 4

Entrepreneurs

Write your answers to questions 1–4 in the blanks provided.

1. How does the following quotation relate to the success of some entrepreneurs?

   Necessity is the mother of invention.
   —Plato

   _____

   _____

   _____

   _____

   _____

2. Some economists say that entrepreneurship is something that cannot be taught but, instead, is a natural talent that some people have. Do you agree? Why or why not?

   _____

   _____

   _____

   _____

   _____

3. Bill Gates, Mark Zuckerberg, and Ted Turner are entrepreneurs whose work has made them among the wealthiest people in the world. Why is it necessary to allow entrepreneurs to benefit from their work?

   _____

   _____

   _____

   _____

   _____

4. How do we all benefit from the work of entrepreneurs?

_____

_____

_____

_____

_____

_____

Milton Friedman and the Free Enterprise System

The Economics in the Real World feature from this section discussed the differences between being pro-business and pro-free enterprise and used a quote from Milton Friedman to explain those concepts. Milton Friedman (1912–2006) won the Nobel Prize in Economics in 1976. He was a highly respected economist, as well as an economist that was known by much of the public. As a professional economist, he was best known for his work on the consumption function (which explains how consumption is related to income), monetary theory and policy, and the degree to which government stabilization policy would or would not work. He was a major proponent of the free enterprise economic system, arguing persuasively that it was the best economic system possible for improving the lives of ordinary people. Not only did Friedman argue that free enterprise was the best system for increasing the material standard of living of people, but that it is also a largely moral economic system since it allows personal choice, voluntary exchange, and open markets. Friedman argued persuasively that government often interferes with or restrains peoples' economic freedoms and, as a result, often numerous undesirable unintended consequences arise.

Write your answer to questions 5 and 6 in the blanks provided.

5. Analyze the importance of Milton Friedman and explain his impact on the U.S. free enterprise system.

_____

_____

_____

_____

_____

6. Why might entrepreneurs particularly appreciate the views of Milton Friedman?

_____

_____

_____

_____

_____

CHAPTER 3, SECTION 5

The Role of Government in a Free Enterprise Economy

Terms

Fill in the blanks in questions 1–7 to be sure you understand some important economic terms.

1. One person's consumption of a(n) _____ takes away from another person's consumption.

2. Individuals can be excluded (physically prohibited) from consuming a(n) _____

   or a(n) _____.

3. Individuals cannot be excluded (physically prohibited) from consuming a(n)

   _____.

4. In a free enterprise economy, firms will not produce _____ because people will not pay for them.

5. A(n) _____ receives the benefits of a good without paying for it.

6. A positive externality is a(n) _____ of an action that is felt by others.

7. A negative externality is a(n) _____ of an act that is felt by others.

Types of Goods

Use the following key to label each of the goods in questions 8–15 as a private good, an excludable public good, or a nonexcludable public good.

  P = private good
  E = excludable public good
  N = nonexcludable public good

8. _____ fireworks display

9. _____ public radio

10. _____ portable mp3 player with earbuds

11. _____ dam

12. _____ toll road

13. _____ national defense

14. _____ rock concert

15. _____ hamburger

Externalities

Use the following key to label each of the situations described in questions 16–23 as a positive externality or a negative externality. Then explain why the externality is positive or negative.

P = positive externality
N = negative externality

16. _____ Your neighbor has loud parties late into the night, keeping you awake.

_____

_____

17. _____ Your neighbor has a large oak tree that shades your yard.

_____

_____

18. _____ Your neighbor does not take care of his house; the house is literally falling apart.

_____

_____

19. _____ Your community has excellent schools.

_____

_____

20. _____ The person sitting next to you in a restaurant is talking loudly on a cell phone.

_____

_____

21. _____ A factory in your town spews pollution into the air.

_____

_____

22. _____ Your state requires children to get vaccinated for common diseases.

_____

_____

23. _____ People in your community shoplift at local stores.

_____

_____

Write your answers to questions 24 and 25 in the blanks provided.

24. How can government encourage the production of positive externalities?

_____

_____

25. How can government discourage the production of negative externalities?

_____

_____

A negative externality places some costs on third parties. A negative externality is **internalized** if the party that generates the negative externality is made to feel the costs of the negative externality. To illustrate, suppose Johnson smokes cigarettes and imposes a negative externality on Smith. Let's go further and say this negative externality is equal to a cost of $2 (as far as Smith is concerned). If Johnson can be made to bear this $2 cost, then the negative externality has been internalized.

You might want to think of internalizing a negative externality the same way you think of a boomerang. When you throw a boomerang outward from you, it returns to you (assuming it was thrown correctly). Johnson "throws" the smoke outward from his cigarette, and while the smoke does not return to him, the cost of the smoke to a third party does revert to him.

With this as background, assume you live in a large city where most people use cars as their means of transportation. As the city has grown, air pollution problems have worsened from the additional cars on the crowded highways. Some people complain to the city council about respiratory problems caused by the pollution.

In response, the city council is considering various solutions to the pollution problem. Members of the council have proposed the following three solutions.

Proposal 1: The solution is to add highway lanes. The money for highway lane construction would come from an increase in the general sales tax.

Proposal 2: The solution is to build a railroad commuter line. The revenue to build the railroad commuter line would come from an increase in the general sales tax.

Proposal 3: The solution is to impose a tax on drivers for driving.

Use the information above and your knowledge of externalities to analyze the problem and the proposals. Write your answers to questions 26–31 in the blanks provided.

26. What negative externality exists here?

_____

_____

27. Will the negative externality be reduced or eliminated by proposal 1? Explain.

_____

_____

_____

_____

28. Will the negative externality be internalized by proposal 1? Explain.

_____

_____

_____

29. Will the negative externality be reduced or eliminated by proposal 2? Explain.

_____

_____

_____

30. Will the negative externality be internalized by proposal 2? Explain.

_____

_____

_____

31. Will the negative externality be internalized by proposal 3? Explain.

_____

_____

_____

_____

Apply what you have learned in this section by completing the following extension activity.

32. Write a Definition and Create a Concept Map Look up the vocabulary words _excludable_, _non-excludable_, and _externality_ in a dictionary and break the words down into their roots and affixes. On a piece of paper, write down what each affix and root means. Then, using accessible language, write a definition for each vocabulary word.

The class will divide into four groups, one for each of the following four terms: _excludable public goods_, _non-excludable public goods_, _positive externalities_, and _negative externalities_. Collaborate with your group to create a concept map of the term to which you are assigned. Place the term in the center and fill in the concept map with examples from your own experience. When all the groups are finished, display the concept maps in the classroom. Review each of the concept maps to confirm your understanding of the terms.

CHAPTER 4, SECTION 1
Demand!

Demand and the Law of Demand

To be sure you understand demand and the law of demand, fill in the blanks in questions 1–4.

1. The two conditions of demand are _____ and

   _____.

2. The law of demand says that as the price of a good increases, the quantity demanded of the good

   _____.

3. The law of demand says that as the price of a good decreases, the quantity demanded of the good

   _____.

4. According to the law of demand, price and quantity demanded move in _____
   direction(s).

Demand Schedules and Demand Curves

The law of demand can be represented in numbers using a **demand schedule** or it can
be represented as a graph showing a **demand curve.**

Answer question 5 to illustrate the connection between a demand schedule and a demand curve.

5. Use the demand schedule below to create a
   demand curve for Simon's consumption of
   music downloads on the grid shown. Label the
   curve D_1.

   DEMAND SCHEDULE FOR SIMON

Price (dollars)	Quantity demanded (units)
$7	1
$6	2
$5	3
$4	4
$3	5
$2	6
$1	7

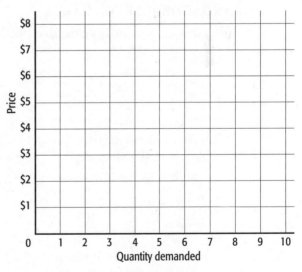

Demand Curve Derived from Demand Schedule

Use the graph you created in question 5 to answer questions 6–10.

6. The demand curve shows that at a price of $7, Simon will buy _____ music download(s), and at a price of $1, he will buy _____ music download(s).

7. Simon's buying behavior demonstrates the law of _____.

8. Simon's change in buying behavior at different prices is a change in _____.

9. Simon is not willing to pay $7 for every download because his utility (satisfaction) decreases as he downloads more and more music. Economists call this concept the

   _____.

10. How does the concept in question 9 explain the slope of the demand curve?

   _____

   _____

   _____

All people do not have the same demand for a good. Some people have a greater willingness and ability to purchase a good than other people do.

Use the information in question 11 to compare the demand curves of two different people for the same good.

11. Use the demand schedule below to create a demand curve for Carla's consumption of music downloads. Draw the graph on the grid shown. Label the curve D_2.

DEMAND SCHEDULE FOR CARLA

Price (dollars)	Quantity demanded (units)
$7	4
$6	5
$5	6
$4	7
$3	8
$2	9
$1	10

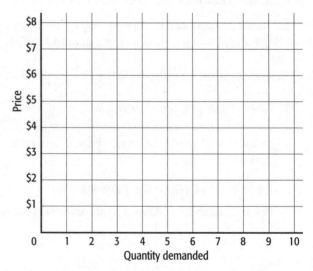

Demand Curve Derived from Demand Schedule

To answer questions 12–15, use the graph in questions 5 and 11, which shows Simon's and Carla's demand curves.

12. For each of the listed prices (for example, $2), Carla is willing and able to buy _____ music downloads than Simon is willing and able to buy.

13. At each of the possible quantities (for example, 5 music downloads), Carla is willing and able to pay a _____ price than Simon is willing and able to pay.

14. The demand curves you created on the grid in questions 5 and 11 are _____ demand curves.

15. Suppose Simon and Carla are the only buyers of music downloads. How would you create a market demand curve from the demand curves you drew on the grids in questions 5 and 11?

_____

_____

_____

Apply what you have learned in this section by completing the following extension activities.

16. **Collaborate to Learn Vocabulary** Working in a small group, use your prior knowledge to make a list of all the different meanings of the words *demand* and *market*. Collaborate to write a sentence using each meaning. Review the definitions of *demand* and *market* in your book. Then watch the business report segment of a recent episode of a nightly news program. Note the context of all uses of the words *demand* and *market*.

    Take turns reading one sentence each from an article in a business or financial newspaper or magazine. Try to mimic the intonation of the newscaster on the nightly news report. If you are not sure how to pronounce a word, attempt to sound it out. If you are still having trouble, ask for assistance from your peers or a teacher. Then re-read the sentence, pronouncing the word correctly.

17. **Write a Narrative** Conduct an interview with a partner in which you ask your partner to tell you about a time when he or she experienced the effects of diminishing marginal utility: that is, a time when the more he or she got of something, the less he or she enjoyed it. Take notes on what your partner says and ask for clarification if you are unsure of his or her meaning. When you have finished your interview, switch roles and let your partner interview you.

    Write a narrative that retells and summarizes your partner's story. When you have finished, have your partner read it and tell you whether or not you captured his or her spoken message accurately. Correct your narrative based on the feedback you receive.

CHAPTER 4, SECTION 2

The Demand Curve Shifts

Changes in Demand and Shifts in Demand Curves

When demand changes, the demand curve shifts. Fill in the blanks in questions 1 and 2 with the correct answers.

1. If demand increases, the demand curve shifts _____, meaning that buyers want to buy _____ of a good at each and every price.

2. If demand decreases, the demand curve shifts _____, meaning that buyers want to buy _____ of a good at each and every price.

Factors That Cause Shifts in Demand Curves

In questions 3–7, list five factors that cause demand curves to shift. For each factor, describe how the factor affects the demand for a good (whether the factor causes demand to rise or fall).

3. *Factor:*

   _____

   Description:

   _____

   _____

4. *Factor:*

   _____

   Description:

   _____

   _____

5. *Factor:*

   _____

   Description:

   _____

   _____

   _____

6. *Factor:*

_____

Description:

_____

_____

7. *Factor:*

_____

Description:

_____

_____

Demand Versus Quantity Demanded

Demand is not the same as quantity demanded. Answer questions 8–11 on the lines provided.

8. What will cause a change in the demand for a good?

_____

_____

9. What will cause a change in the quantity demanded of a good?

_____

_____

10. How is a change in demand represented on a graph?

_____

_____

11. How is a change in quantity demanded represented on a graph?

_____

_____

Changes in Demand and in Quantity Demanded

In questions 12–17, fill in the blanks to describe how each event will affect the demand for large sport utility vehicles (SUVs).

12. The price of gasoline hits $5 per gallon.

Will the demand for large SUVs increase, decrease, or stay the same?

_____

In which direction will the demand curve shift?

_____

Which of the five factors causes the shift?

_____

13. Smaller, sportier "crossover vehicles" hit the market and become the latest craze.

Will the demand for large SUVs increase, decrease, or stay the same?

_____

In which direction will the demand curve shift?

_____

Which of the five factors causes the shift?

_____

14. Rising steel prices cause the prices of SUVs to rise.

Will the demand for large SUVs increase, decrease, or stay the same?

_____

In which direction will the demand curve shift?

_____

_____

Which of the five factors causes the shift?

_____

15. Government data show that the incomes of Americans are expected to rise faster than ever over the next year.

Will the demand for large SUVs increase, decrease, or stay the same?

_____

In which direction will the demand curve shift?

_____

Which of the five factors causes the shift?

_____

16. Word leaks to consumers that General Motors and Ford plan to offer big rebates on SUVs next month.

Will the current demand for large SUVs increase, decrease, or stay the same?

_____

In which direction will the demand curve shift?

_____

Which of the five factors causes the shift?

_____

17. The government loosens immigration laws, allowing millions of immigrants into the country. Will the demand for large SUVs increase, decrease, or stay the same?

_____

In which direction will the demand curve shift?

_____

Which of the five factors causes the shift?

_____

The Relationship Between Income and Demand

As a result of an increase in wages from his employer, Kramer increased his consumption of Junior Mints and Bosco chocolate-flavored syrup, decreased his consumption of fried chicken, and maintained the same consumption of yogurt.

In questions 18–21, identify each of the goods consumed by Kramer as a normal good, an inferior good, or a neutral good.

18. Junior Mints _____

19. Bosco chocolate-flavored syrup _____

20. fried chicken _____

21. yogurt _____

In questions 22–25, identify which one of graphs (a), (b), and (c) illustrates the change to Kramer's demand curve for each of the goods.

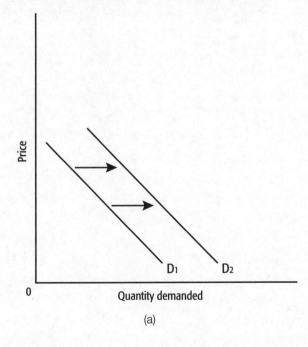

(a)

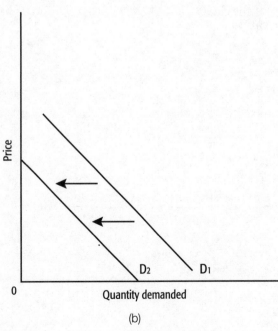

(b)

22. Junior Mints _____

23. Bosco chocolate-flavored syrup _____

24. fried chicken _____

25. yogurt _____

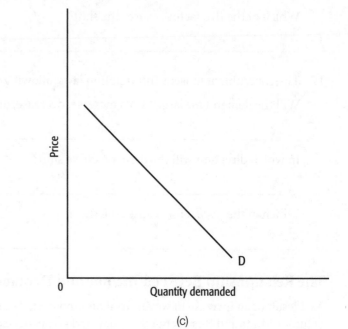

(c)

Apply what you have learned in this section by completing the following extension activity.

26. Present a TV Report Using local newspapers and TV news shows, research the housing market in your area. Is the demand curve for houses shifting? If so, in what direction? Use information from your research to infer the reasons for the shift (or the lack thereof). Based on your findings, make a prediction about what you think will happen to the local housing market in the next year.

Using formal English, a variety of sentence types and lengths, and relevant content-based vocabulary and key words (such as market, demand, and supply), prepare a short TV news report in which you identify the current trend in the local housing market, give your prediction for the market in the next year, and explain the reasons for your prediction. Practice giving your report to a classmate, and ask for feedback on your pronunciation, intonation, and pacing. If asked, present your report to the class.

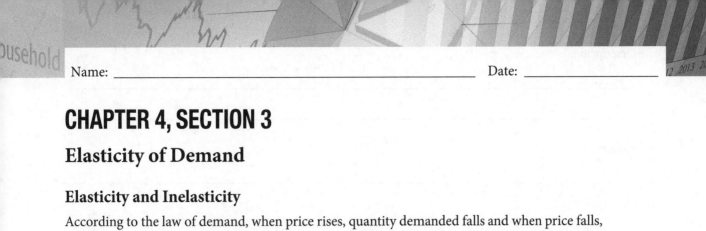

CHAPTER 4, SECTION 3

Elasticity of Demand

Elasticity and Inelasticity

According to the law of demand, when price rises, quantity demanded falls and when price falls, quantity demanded rises. Elasticity of demand is a measure of *how much* the quantity demanded of a good rises or falls due to a change in the price of the good.

You can think of elastic demand as being like an elastic band—the quantity demanded of the good will stretch freely when pulled by a change in the good's price. Inelastic demand is more like a rope—the quantity demanded of the good will not stretch easily when pulled by a change in the good's price.

In questions 1 and 2, circle the letter of the correct answer.

1. If the price of a good with elastic demand increases, which of the following describes the effect on the quantity demanded of the good?

    a. increases a little

    b. increases a lot

    c. decreases a little

    d. decreases a lot

2. If the price of a good with inelastic demand increases, which of the following describes the effect on the quantity demanded of the good?

    a. increases a little

    b. increases a lot

    c. decreases a little

    d. decreases a lot

Factors That Determine Elasticity of Demand

In questions 3–6, list the four factors that determine the elasticity of demand. For each factor, describe how the factor affects the elasticity of demand for a good (that is, explain whether it causes demand to be more elastic or more inelastic).

3. *Factor:*

    _____

    Description:

    _____

    _____

4. *Factor:*

    _____

Description:

_____

_____

5. *Factor:*

_____

Description:

_____

_____

6. *Factor:*

_____

Description:

_____

_____

Considering the factors you listed in questions 3–6, identify the demand for the goods in questions 7–9 as elastic, inelastic, or unit-elastic. Explain the reason for each choice.

7. T-bone steak

_____

_____

8. new sports car

_____

_____

9. insulin

_____

_____

In each of the cases described in questions 10–12, identify whether the demand for the good is elastic, inelastic, or unit-elastic. Write your answers on the lines provided.

10. _____ The price of corn rises 5 percent, and the quantity demanded falls 15 percent.

11. _____ The price of bagels rises 8 percent, and the quantity demanded falls 8 percent.

12. _____ The price of telephones rises 10 percent, and the quantity demanded falls 2 percent.

Elasticity and Total Revenue

Elasticity of demand matters to sellers of goods because it relates to their total revenue (Price × Quantity sold = Total revenue). Questions 13–19 relate to how the elasticity of demand for a good affects a seller's total revenue when the seller changes the price of the good. Fill in each blank with the correct answer.

13. If demand for a good is *elastic* and price increases, then total revenue will

    _____.

14. If demand for a good is *elastic* and price decreases, then total revenue will

    _____.

15. If demand for a good is *inelastic* and price increases, then total revenue will

    _____.

16. If demand for a good is *inelastic* and price decreases, then total revenue will

    _____.

17. If demand for a good is *unit-elastic* and price increases, then total revenue will

    _____.

18. If demand for a good is *unit-elastic* and price decreases, then total revenue will

    _____.

19. If a seller would like to increase revenue, the seller should (a) increase the price of the good if the

    demand for the good is _____ *or* (b) decrease the price of the good if the demand

    for the good is _____.

In each of questions 20–22, complete the table to calculate the total revenue for the good. Then fill in the blanks in the question following the table to summarize the results in each case.

20. When Edith increased the price of a good from $2 to $3, the quantity demanded rose from 100 to 110.

	Price	×	Quantity sold	=	Total revenue
Original	$_____		_____		$_____
New	$_____		_____		$_____

    So, because revenue _____ when the price _____, demand

    for the good must be _____.

21. When Renaldo increased the price from $10 to $12, the quantity demanded fell from 80 to 40.

	Price	×	Quantity sold	=	Total revenue
Original	$_____		_____		$_____
New	$_____		_____		$_____

    So, because revenue _____ when the price _____, demand

    for the good must be _____.

22. When Keiko decreased the price from $150 to $125, the quantity demanded rose from 60 to 120.

	Price	×	Quantity sold	=	Total revenue
Original	$_____		_____		$_____
New	$_____		_____		$_____

So, because revenue _____ when the price _____, demand

for the good must be _____.

Elasticity of Demand and a Cigarette User Fee

Suppose your state legislature places a $1 tax on each pack of cigarettes sold. Use this information and your knowledge of elasticity of demand to answer questions 23–26.

23. If the price of a pack of cigarettes rises by $1, and the quantity of cigarettes purchased by consumers decreases from 10,000 packs of cigarettes (for the whole population) a day to 9,950 packs of cigarettes, then is the demand for cigarettes likely to be inelastic or elastic?

    _____

    _____

24. Given the large increase in price, in which income groups and age groups would you expect to see the greatest decrease in quantity demanded?

    _____

    _____

    _____

25. Which of the four factors that determine elasticity of demand do you think plays the largest role in people's demand for cigarettes?

    _____

    _____

    _____

26. How might time affect this scenario?

    _____

    _____

Elasticity of Demand and Gas Prices

Many people believe that an increase in the price of gasoline will change consumer attitudes and driving behavior. They assume people will drive less often and buy smaller, more efficient cars as the price of gasoline increases. However, imagine that gas prices increased significantly and people's driving habits and gas consumption levels changed very little. Use this information and your knowledge about elasticity of demand to answer questions 27–29.

27. Is the demand for gasoline more elastic or more inelastic than previously thought? Explain your answer.

   _____

   _____

   _____

   _____

28. Which of the four factors that determine elasticity of demand do you think plays the largest role in people's buying habits for gasoline?

   _____

   _____

   _____

29. How might time affect this scenario?

   _____

   _____

   _____

CHAPTER 4
We Demand Practice!

In each of questions 1–14, an event has occurred that will affect the demand or quantity demanded for a good. Illustrate the change in demand or quantity demanded for the good that is listed below the graph. To illustrate a change in demand (also called a shift of the demand curve), draw a parallel line to the right or left of the original line plus an arrow to indicate direction of the shift. To illustrate a change in the quantity demanded (also called a movement along the demand curve), indicate two points on the demand curve and draw an arrow pointing up or down the curve between the two points.

1. The Hunger Games movies increase interest in the books.

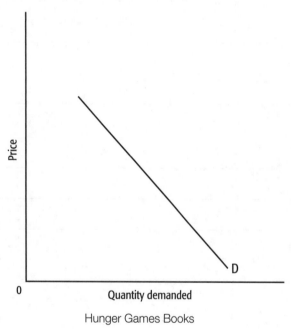

Hunger Games Books

2. Gas prices have risen to new high levels.

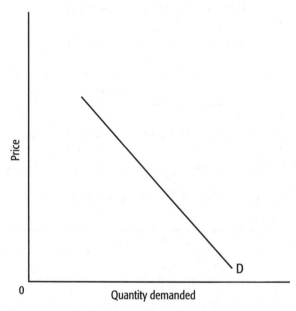

Motor Scooters with High Miles per Gallon

3. The price of beef is expected to rise next week.

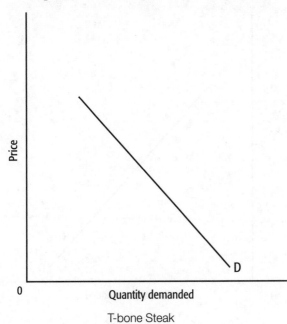

T-bone Steak

4. The price of beef rises.

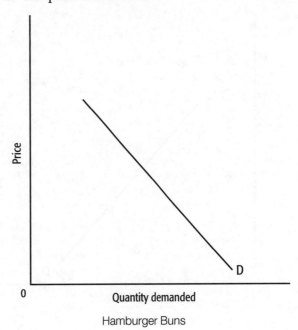

Hamburger Buns

5. The first snowstorm of the season occurs.

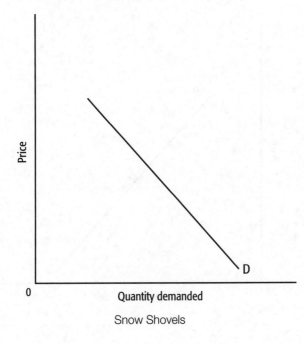

Snow Shovels

6. Summer vacation begins!

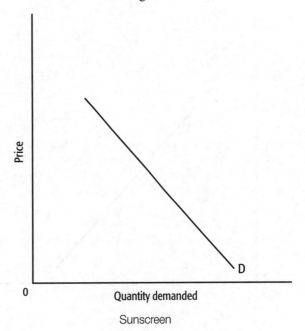

Sunscreen

7. A tax rebate increases incomes.

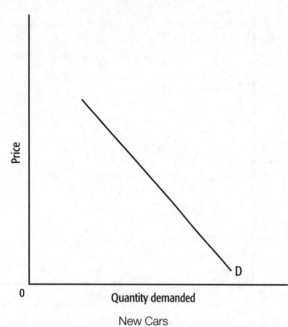

New Cars

8. The price of pork rises.

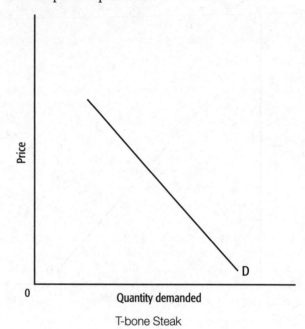

T-bone Steak

9. The price of Blu-ray players decreases.

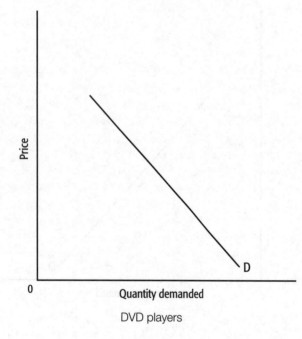

DVD players

10. The price of Blu-ray players decreases.

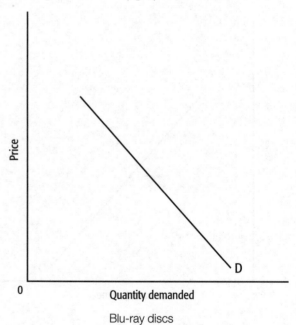

Blu-ray discs

Applying the Principles Workbook

11. The price of breakfast cereal rises.

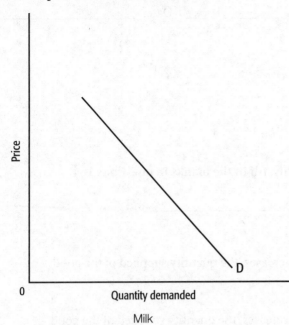

Milk

12. The price of orange juice rises.

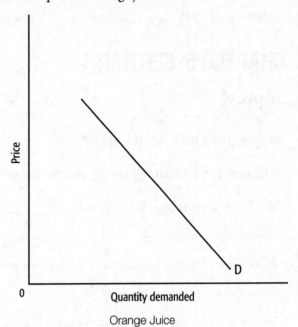

Orange Juice

13. The price of orange juice rises.

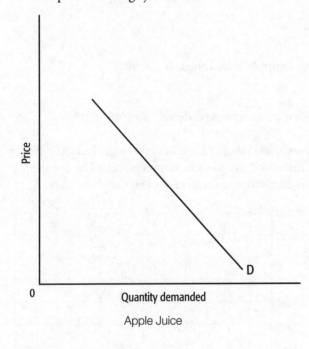

Apple Juice

14. Tiger Woods creates a new fad: golf.

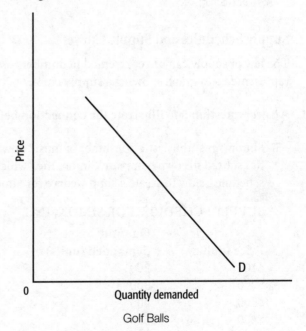

Golf Balls

Name: _____ Date: _____

CHAPTER 5, SECTION 1
Supply!

Supply and the Law of Supply

To be sure you understand supply and the law of supply, fill in the blanks in questions 1–4.

1. The two conditions of supply are _____ and
   _____.

2. The law of supply says that as the price of a good increases, the quantity supplied of the good
   _____.

3. The law of supply says that as the price of a good decreases, the quantity supplied of the good
   _____.

4. According to the law of supply, price and quantity supplied move in _____
   direction(s).

Supply Schedules and Supply Curves

The law of supply can be represented in numbers using a **supply schedule** or it can be
represented as a graph showing a **supply curve**.

Answer question 5 to illustrate the connection between a supply schedule and a supply curve.

5. Simon, an enthusiastic consumer of music downloads, has taken a keen interest in the industry. He
   has started his own company, Simon, Inc., which manufactures premium mp3 players. Use the supply
   schedule below to create a supply curve for Simon's company on the grid shown. Label the curve S_1.

SUPPLY SCHEDULE FOR SIMON, INC.

Price (dollars)	Quantity demanded (units)
$100	200
$200	300
$300	400
$400	500
$500	600
$600	700
$700	800

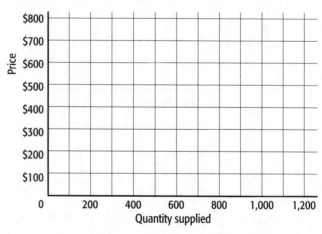

Supply Curve Derived from Supply Schedule

Applying the Principles Workbook   © EMC Publishing

Use the graph you created in question 5 to answer questions 6–8.

6. The supply curve shows that at a price of $300, Simon, Inc., will offer to sell _____ premium mp3 players, and at a price of $600, the company will offer to sell _____ premium mp3 players.

7. The company's selling behavior demonstrates the law of _____.

8. The change in production of Simon, Inc., at different prices is a change in _____.

All producers do not supply the same amount of a good. Some are willing and able to supply greater quantities than others are.

Use the information in question 9 to compare the supply curves of two different companies for the same good.

9. Use the supply schedule below to create a supply curve for premium mp3 players for Carla, Inc. Draw the graph on the grid shown. Label the curve S₂.

SUPPLY SCHEDULE FOR CARLA, INC.

Price (dollars)	Quantity supplied (units)
$100	400
$200	500
$300	600
$400	700
$500	800
$600	900
$700	1,000

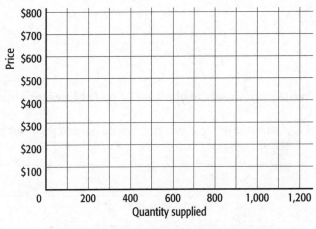

Supply Curve Derived from Supply Schedule

To answer questions 10–13, use the graphs in question 5 and 9, which show the supply curves for both Simon, Inc., and Carla, Inc.

10. For each of the listed prices (for example, $400), Carla, Inc., is willing and able to produce _____ premium mp3 players than Simon, Inc., is willing and able to produce.

11. At each of the possible quantities (for example, 600), Carla, Inc., is willing to accept a _____ price than Simon, Inc., is willing to accept.

12. The supply curves you created on the grids in question 5 and 9 are _____ supply curves.

13. Suppose Simon, Inc., and Carla, Inc., are the only suppliers of premium mp3 players. How would you create a market supply curve from the supply curves you drew on the grids in questions 5 and 9?

_____

_____

_____

Vertical Supply Curves

As shown in the figure to the right, a supply curve is vertical when the quantity supplied cannot increase regardless of the price. For instance, the number of tickets available for this season's Super Bowl is finite because the stadium has a fixed number of seats. A vertical supply curve illustrates that at any price, the quantity supplied remains the same.

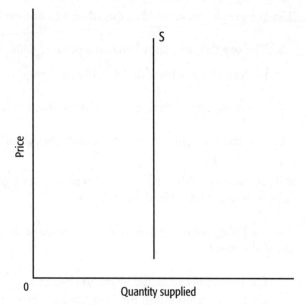

Supply Curve When Quantity Supplied Cannot Increase

Write your answer to question 14 on the lines provided.

14. List three other goods that would have vertical supply curves.

_____

_____

_____

CHAPTER 5, SECTION 2
The Supply Curve Shifts

Changes in Supply and Shifts in Supply Curves

When supply changes, the supply curve shifts. Fill in the blanks in questions 1 and 2 with the correct answers.

1. If supply increases, the supply curve shifts _____, meaning that sellers want to sell _____ of a good at each and every price.

2. If supply decreases, the supply curve shifts _____, meaning that sellers want to sell _____ of a good at each and every price.

Factors That Cause Shifts in Demand Curves

In questions 3–10, list the factors that cause supply curves to shift. For each factor, describe how the factor affects the supply of a good (whether the factor causes supply to rise or to fall).

3. *Factor:*

_____

Description:

_____

_____

4. *Factor:*

_____

Description:

_____

_____

5. *Factor:*

_____

Description:

_____

_____

6. *Factor:*

_____

Description:

_____

_____

7. *Factor:*

_____

Description:

_____

_____

8. *Factor:*

_____

Description:

_____

_____

9. *Factor:*

_____

Description:

_____

_____

_____

_____

10. *Factor:*

_____

Description:

_____

_____

Supply Versus Quantity Supplied

Supply is not the same as quantity supplied. Answer questions 11–14 on the lines provided.

11. What will cause a change in the supply of a good?

_____

_____

12. What will cause a change in the quantity supplied of a good?

_____

_____

13. How is a change in supply represented on a graph?

_____

_____

14. How is a change in quantity supplied represented on a graph?

_____

_____

Changes in Supply and in Quantity Supplied

In questions 15–23, fill in the blanks to describe how each event will affect the country's total supply of corn.

15. The U.S. government increases the subsidy for corn production.

Will the supply of corn increase, decrease, or stay the same?

_____

In which direction will the supply curve shift?

_____

Which of the eight factors causes the shift?

_____

16. A major drought destroys crops in America's heartland.

Will the supply of corn increase, decrease, or stay the same?

_____

In which direction will the supply curve shift?

_____

Which of the eight factors causes the shift?

_____

17. The price of fuel used in farm machinery increases to a new high.

Will the supply of corn increase, decrease, or stay the same?

_____

In which direction will the supply curve shift?

_____

Which of the eight factors causes the shift?

_____

18. The U.S. government places a quota on all imported farm products.

Will the supply of corn increase, decrease, or stay the same?

_____

In which direction will the supply curve shift?

_____

Which of the eight factors causes the shift?

_____

19. A newly developed seed increases the corn yield.

Will the supply of corn increase, decrease, or stay the same?

_____

In which direction will the supply curve shift?

_____

Which of the eight factors causes the shift?

_____

20. As property values rise, many farm fields are turned into housing developments and shopping malls.

Will the supply of corn increase, decrease, or stay the same?

_____

In which direction will the supply curve shift?

_____

Which of the eight factors causes the shift?

_____

21. The U.S. government gives farmers a tax cut by allowing them to deduct most expenses.

Will the supply of corn increase, decrease, or stay the same?

_____

In which direction will the supply curve shift?

_____

Which of the eight factors causes the shift?

_____

22. Corn prices are expected to rise next month as more ethanol refineries start production.
    Will the current supply of corn increase, decrease, or stay the same?

    _____

    In which direction will the supply curve shift?

    _____

    Which of the eight factors causes the shift?

    _____

23. Chocolate-covered corn on a stick becomes a new fad at state fairs.
    Will the supply of corn increase, decrease, or stay the same?

    _____

    In which direction will the supply curve shift?

    _____

    Which of the eight factors causes the shift?

    _____

Elasticity of Supply

Elasticity of supply is a measure of *how much* the quantity supplied of a good rises or
falls owing to a change in the price of the good.

Fill in the blanks in questions 24–26 with the correct answers.

24. When quantity supplied changes by a larger percentage than price, supply is _____.

25. When quantity supplied changes by a smaller percentage than price, supply is

    _____.

26. When quantity supplied changes by the same percentage as price, supply is _____.

Elasticity Versus Inelasticity

**In each of the cases described in questions 27–29, identify whether the supply of the good is
elastic, inelastic, or unit-elastic.**

27. _____ The price of textbooks increases by 20 percent, and the quantity supplied
    of textbooks rises 20 percent.

28. _____ The price of jeans increases by 5 percent, and the quantity supplied of
    jeans increases by 3 percent.

29. _____ The price of TVs increases by 15 percent, and the quantity supplied of
    TVs increases by 25 percent.

Write your answers to questions 30 and 31 on the lines provided.

30. Given that it takes many months to build a house, do you think the supply of houses is more elastic in the short run or the long run?

_____

_____

31. Will the supply curve for most goods become more vertical or more horizontal as time passes?

_____

_____

Apply what you have learned in this section by completing the following extension activities.

32. **Present Testimony** View at least two objective reports about U.S. farm subsidies. Take notes on the main points of the reports. You may need to view each report more than once.

     Imagine that you are going to testify before Congress about whether farm subsidies have a positive or negative effect on the U.S. economy. Analyze the information you learned in the reports you viewed to determine your opinion on the effects of farm subsidies. Prepare your testimony using academic words such as *subsidy* and *incentive* and then present your testimony to the class. After you have finished your presentation, take and respond to questions from the class.

33. **Write about a Storm's Economic Impact** With a partner, brainstorm and discuss what you already know about Hurricane Sandy. Next, locate a newspaper or magazine article about Hurricane Sandy's effect on the supply of goods throughout America. Take turns reading the article aloud, one paragraph at a time. If there are any words or terms you don't understand, work together to look up the meanings. Then read the article again silently. If there is any vocabulary you still don't understand, ask for help from your partner or a teacher.

     Working on your own, write a paragraph explaining Hurricane Sandy's effect on the supply of goods throughout America. Define any content-related words or terms for the reader.

34. **Collaborate to Value Art** Collaborate with a small group to identify paintings (an item for which supply is inelastic) that have sold for over 100 million dollars in the last 40 years. Assign each group member one painting to research. Prepare to conduct your research by brainstorming the factors that might make a painting valuable. Use a graphic organizer, such as an idea web, to organize the results of your brainstorming. Then, working on your own, research why your assigned painting is so valuable. You might choose to read materials from reliable sources, view related media items, or both. Take notes on your findings, using content-based vocabulary words where appropriate.

     When all group members have completed their research, take turns summarizing your findings for the group. After all group members have presented their findings, work together to compile a list of the main factors that make a painting valuable. Don't forget to consider the supply of paintings by the same artist. When you have finished your list, compare it with those of other groups by discussing your findings as a class.

CHAPTER 5

Supply Practice!

In each of questions 1–14, an event has occurred that will affect the supply or quantity supplied of a good. Illustrate the change in supply or quantity supplied for the good that is listed below the graph. To illustrate a change in supply (also called a shift of the supply curve), draw a parallel line to the right or left of the original line, plus an arrow to indicate the direction of the shift. To illustrate a change in the quantity supplied (also called a movement along the supply curve), indicate two points on the supply curve, and draw an arrow pointing up or down the curve between the two points.

1. Soybean prices are expected to rise next month.

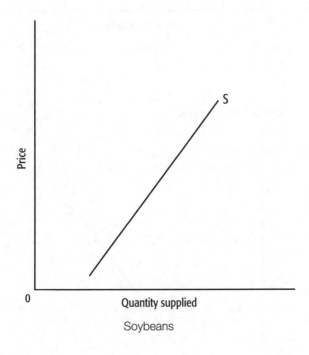

Soybeans

2. The government decides to subsidize oil companies.

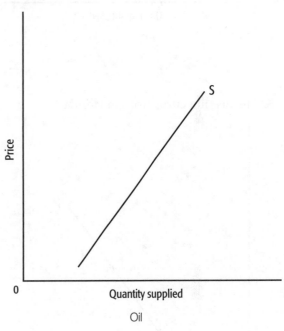

Oil

3. The autoworkers union wins higher pay for workers.

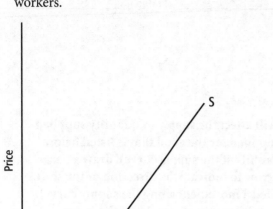

4. The government places a quota on imported textiles.

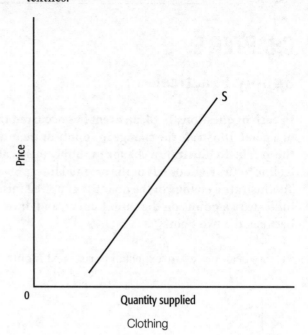

5. Storms ruin citrus crops in Florida.

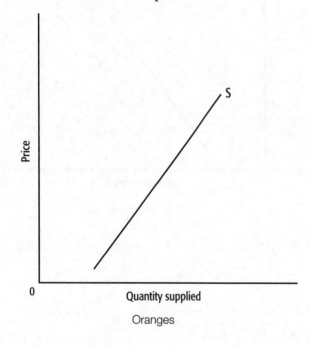

6. Steel prices soar.

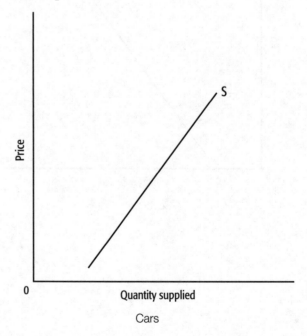

7. Paper prices fall.

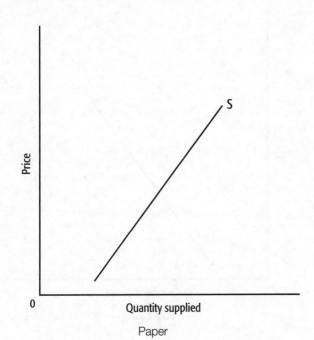

Paper

8. Government increases the tax that cigarette producers pay.

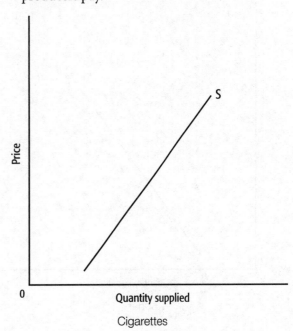

Cigarettes

9. New software increases widget production.

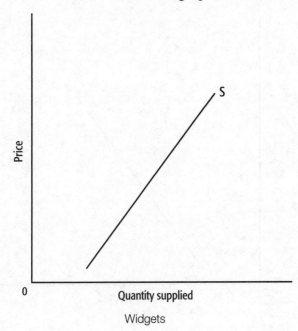

Widgets

10. The price of wheat is expected to fall next week.

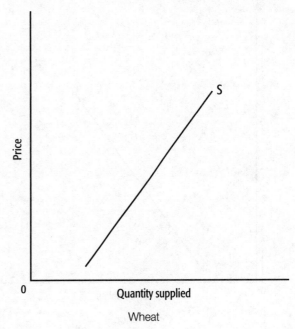

Wheat

11. A new trade agreement eliminates sugar quotas.

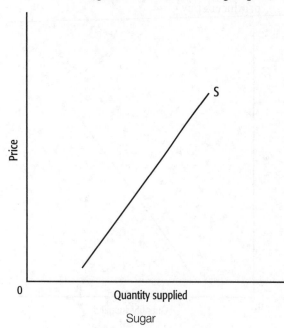

Sugar

12. Lumber prices rise.

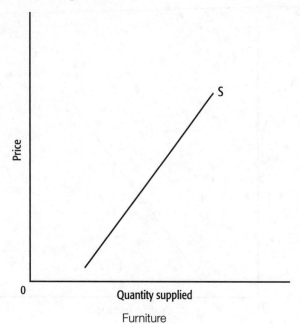

Furniture

13. High profits increase the number of cell phone manufacturers.

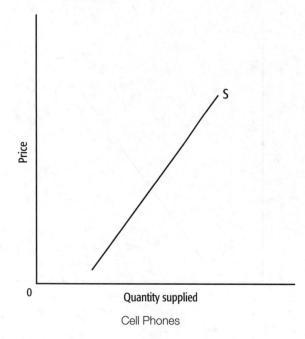

Cell Phones

14. Computer producers find new ways to reduce labor costs.

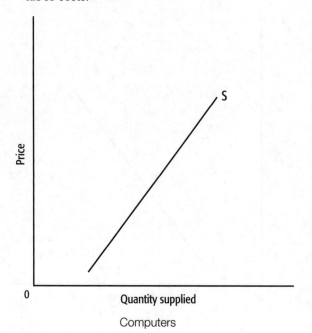

Computers

Name: _____   Date: _____

CHAPTER 6, SECTION 1

Price: Supply and Demand Together

In a market, supply and demand work together to determine the price of a good. Write your answers to questions 1–6 in the blanks provided to be sure you understand the different market conditions and how they affect price.

1. What market condition exists when quantity supplied is greater than quantity demanded?

   _____

2. What happens to price when the market condition in question 1 exists? _____

3. What market condition exists when quantity demanded is greater than quantity supplied?

   _____

4. What happens to price when the market condition in question 3 exists? _____

5. What market condition exists when quantity demanded is equal to quantity supplied?

   _____

6. Do markets tend to move toward shortage, surplus, or equilibrium? _____

Suppose that in the market for gadgets, the quantities demanded and supplied at various prices are as shown in the following table, and answer question 7.

SUPPLY AND DEMAND IN THE GADGET MARKET

| | Quantity | |
Price	Demanded	Supplied
$0.10	450	50
$0.20	400	100
$0.30	350	150
$0.40	300	200
$0.50	250	250
$0.60	200	300
$0.70	150	350
$0.80	100	400

7. Use the information in the table to draw the supply and demand curves for the gadget market on the following grid. Label the vertical axis "Price" and label the horizontal axis "Quantity." Use the prices and quantities demanded in the table to plot the demand curve. Label it D_1. Use the prices and quantities supplied in the table to plot the supply curve. Label it S_1.

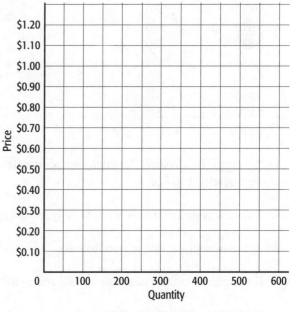

Price: Supply and Demand Together

Use the graph you created in question 7 to answer questions 8–15.

8. The equilibrium price in the gadget market is _____.

9. At the equilibrium price, sellers want to sell _____ gadgets and buyers want to buy _____ gadgets.

10. If the price of gadgets rises to $0.70, sellers will want to sell _____ gadgets and buyers will want to buy _____ gadgets.

11. A price rise to $0.70 will result in a _____ of _____ gadgets.

12. If the market condition in question 11 exists, prices will _____ and price will settle at _____.

13. If the price of gadgets falls to $0.30, sellers will want to sell _____ gadgets and buyers will want to buy _____ gadgets.

14. A price fall to $0.30 will result in a _____ of _____ gadgets.

15. If the market condition in question 13 exists, prices will _____ and price will settle at _____.

Now assume that as a result of changing consumer preferences, gadgets become the newest fad, and respond to questions 16 and 17.

16. Will this change in consumer preferences cause a change in demand or quantity demanded?

    _____

17. Use the demand schedule below to draw a second demand curve on the grid in question 7. Label this second demand curve D_2.

Price	Quantity demanded
$0.10	550
$0.20	500
$0.30	450
$0.40	400
$0.50	350
$0.60	300
$0.70	250
$0.80	200

Use the graph in question 7, which now shows demand curves D_1 and D_2 and supply curve S_1, to answer questions 18–21.

18. The new equilibrium price in the gadget market is _____.

19. At the new price, sellers want to sell _____ gadgets and buyers want to buy _____ gadgets.

20. Is the gadget market described by D_2 and S_1 in a state of shortage, surplus, or equilibrium?

    _____

21. So, as a result of the change in consumer preferences, the price of gadgets increased _____, the quantity demanded increased _____ units, and the quantity supplied increased _____ units.

Price is a way for buyers and sellers to communicate with each other. It signals a change in the market for a good. Fill in each blank in questions 22–25 with the correct word.

22. When a market experiences a shortage, price will _____.

23. When a shortage occurs, supply and demand work together to influence price and move the market toward _____.

24. When a market experiences a surplus, price will _____.

25. When a surplus occurs, supply and demand work together to influence price and move the market toward _____.

Apply what you have learned in this section by completing the following extension activity.

26. **Collaborate to Comprehend** In a small group, read the definitions of the topic-related vocabulary words *surplus* and *shortage*. Using the dictionary, collaborate to break the vocabulary words down into their roots and affixes.

    Next, look at Exhibit 6-3 in your text. Work together to make sure you understand each of the graphs. Ask questions as needed to confirm your understanding. Finally, take turns reading the whole section aloud. If you encounter words you do not know, collaborate to use the context of each word to determine its meaning.

CHAPTER 6, SECTION 1

Price Controls

Fill in the blanks in questions 1 and 2 with the correct words.

1. A price ceiling is a legislated price _____ which legal trades cannot be made.

2. A price floor is a legislated price _____ which legal trades cannot be made.

Rent control is a price ceiling. It is an effort by local government to help the poor by making housing more affordable. The following graph shows apartment rents in a local housing market.

Use the graph to answer questions 3 and 4.

3. The equilibrium price of apartments in this market is _____.

4. The equilibrium quantity of apartments in this market is _____ units.

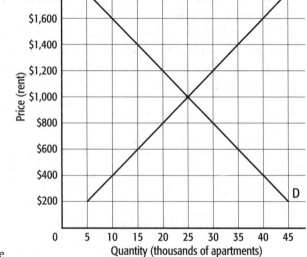

A Housing Market

Now suppose this local government imposes rent controls that require apartments be rented for no more than $600, and respond to question 5.

5. Draw a horizontal line across the graph at a price (rent) of $600 to show this price ceiling.

Questions 6–9 are based on the new graph, which now shows the price ceiling. Write your answers in the blanks provided.

6. At a rent of $600, _____ apartments are demanded and _____ apartments are supplied.

7. The local government intended to help the poor by controlling the price of housing but, instead, has created a _____ of _____ apartments.

8. What happens to many people as a result of the rent control?

_____

_____

9. How could the local government achieve its goal of helping the poor without using rent control?

_____

_____

A minimum wage is a price floor. It is an effort by state or federal government to ensure that workers receive a fair wage for their labor. The following graph shows the wages in a labor market.

Use the graph to answer questions 10 and 11.

10. The equilibrium price of labor in this market is

_____.

11. The equilibrium quantity of labor in this market

is _____ workers.

A Labor Market

**Now, suppose that government imposes a minimum wage of $9 an hour—
no worker can receive a wage of less than $9 an hour—and answer question 12.**

12. Draw a horizontal line across the graph at a price (wage) of $9 to show this price floor.

**Questions 13–16 are based on the new graph, which now shows the price floor.
Write your answers in the blanks provided.**

13. At a wage of $9 an hour, _____ workers are demanded and

_____ workers are supplied.

14. Government intended to help workers by setting a minimum wage but, instead, has created a

_____ of _____ workers.

15. What happens to many workers as a result of the minimum wage? _____.

16. How could government achieve its goal of helping workers without using a minimum wage?

_____

_____

Write your answers to questions 17 and 18 in the blanks provided.

17. If economists generally oppose price controls because of their negative unintended effects, why do you think politicians continue to use them?

_____

_____

_____

_____

18. As a worker who likely would benefit from an increase in the minimum wage, how do you feel about proposals to raise the minimum wage?

_____

_____

Assume legislators in your state passed a law to control the price of gasoline. The law was meant to protect people from suspected price gouging by controlling the maximum price wholesalers could charge for gasoline.

Write your answers to questions 19–21 in the blanks provided.

19. The new law is a _____.

20. Your state will likely experience a _____ of gasoline as a result of the law.

21. If a legislator in your state asked your opinion about the gasoline price control, what would you say?

_____

_____

_____

_____

Apply what you have learned in this section by completing the following extension activities.

22. **Write About Price Controls** Research the use of price controls in the U.S. during World War II, reading your sources silently. If you have trouble understanding language structures in your sources, ask your teacher or classmates for help. Take notes about why price controls were enacted, who controlled the prices, and whether the controls achieved their purpose. Using the information you discovered, write an encyclopedia entry summarizing the use of U.S. price controls in World War II.

    After you have finished writing, edit and revise your encyclopedia entry, paying special attention to spelling. If you are unsure of a word's spelling, look it up in the dictionary. Be sure that you cite your resources and attribute ideas and information to their authors.

23. **Consider Responsive Prices** In a brief essay, explain the benefits of responsive prices within the U.S. free enterprise system and how that process differs from imposed price controls and floors.

CHAPTER 6, SECTION 2
Supply and Demand in Everyday Life

Each of the graphs in questions 1–9 shows supply and demand for the good named in the title of the graph. Then the event described occurs. On the graph, illustrate the shift in the supply curve or the demand curve as a result of the event. Then, fill in the blanks to indicate how equilibrium price and equilibrium quantity change as a result of the event.

1. *Event:* The price of snow skis goes up.

   The equilibrium price of ski boots goes

   _____ and the

   equilibrium quantity of ski boots goes

   _____ .

2. *Event:* A high protein diet fad sweeps the nation.

   The equilibrium price of hamburger goes

   _____ and the

   equilibrium quantity of hamburger goes

   _____ .

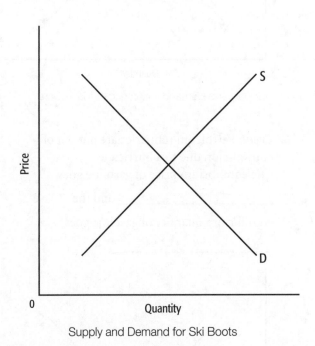

Supply and Demand for Ski Boots

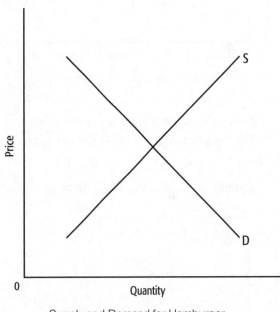

Supply and Demand for Hamburger

3. *Event:* New technologies are introduced in the gadget-manufacturing process.

The equilibrium price of gadgets goes

_____ and the

equilibrium quantity of gadgets goes

_____ .

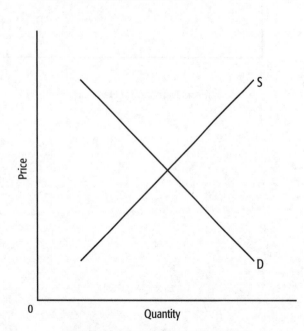

Supply and Demand for Gadgets

4. *Event:* The U.S. government imposes a quota to protect the domestic steel industry.

The equilibrium price of American-made cars

goes _____ and the

equilibrium quantity of American-made cars

goes _____ .

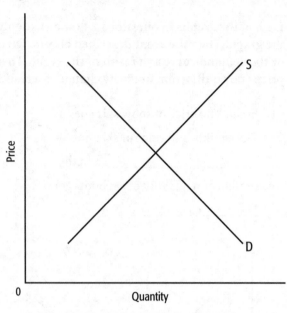

Supply and Demand for American-Made Cars

5. *Event:* The price of Blu-ray players drops. The equilibrium price of DVD discs goes

_____ and the

equilibrium quantity of DVD discs goes

_____ .

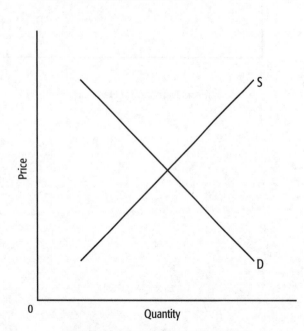

Supply and Demand for DVD discs

6. *Event:* Petroleum refineries are put out of commission due to a hurricane.

The equilibrium price of gasoline goes

_____ and the

equilibrium quantity of gasoline goes

_____ .

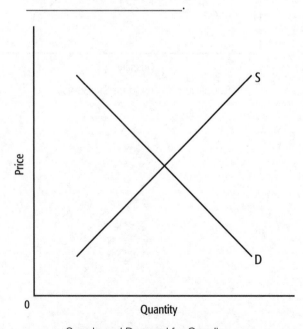

Supply and Demand for Gasoline

7. *Event:* The government increases the amount of the corn subsidy paid to farmers.
The equilibrium price of corn goes

_____ and the

equilibrium quantity of corn goes

_____.

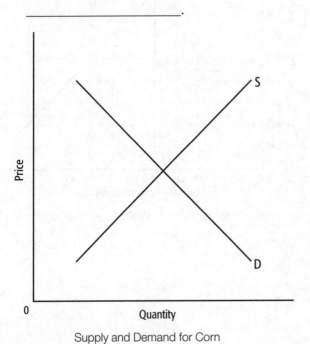

Supply and Demand for Corn

8. *Event:* Consumers expect the price of gasoline to increase tomorrow.
The equilibrium price of gasoline goes

_____ and the

equilibrium quantity of gasoline goes

_____.

Supply and Demand for Gasoline

9. *Event:* Coffee prices increase.
The equilibrium price of tea goes

_____ and the

equilibrium quantity of tea goes

_____.

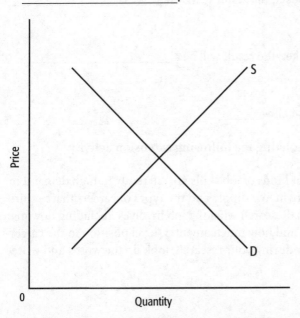

Supply and Demand for Tea As Replacement for Coffee

The following graph shows the market for the reunion tour of a famous 1990s boy band. Use the graph to answer questions 10–15.

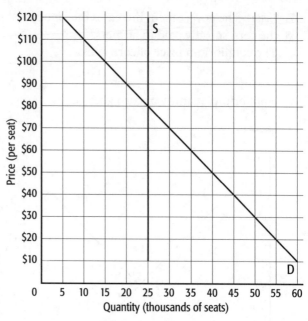

Ticket Price for Famous 1990s Boy Band Concert

10. The equilibrium price is _____.

11. The equilibrium quantity is _____ tickets.

12. Why is the supply curve vertical?

_____

_____

_____

_____

13. If concert organizers decide to charge $100 per ticket, the result will be a _____
    of _____ tickets.

14. If concert organizers decide to charge $60 per ticket, the result will be a _____ of
    _____ tickets.

15. Ticket scalpers will exist only if tickets are priced below _____.

Apply what you have learned in this section by completing the following extension activity.

16. **Present a Promising Career Path** Research what kinds of job skills are currently in high demand in the U.S. Then find out which of these job skills are in low supply and the types of careers that require them. Of these, choose a career that interests you. Research what the job involves, including how many hours of work are required or expected per week and how much an entry-level position in the career pays. If you encounter any unfamiliar vocabulary during your research, look up the words and write down their meanings.

Write an outline for a presentation about the career path you researched. Be sure to include in your outline the job skills the career requires and an explanation of why you think it would be a promising career path to pursue. Using your outline, give a short presentation about the career you researched. If you can't think of the exact English words as you are speaking, use synonyms and circumlocution—that is, use words you know to describe those you don't. When you have finished, take and respond to questions from your classmates.

Listen carefully to your classmates' presentations. Monitor your comprehension and ask questions as needed to clarify your understanding of each career path.

CHAPTER 7, SECTION 1

About Business Firms

Necessity of Bosses

Write your answers to questions 1 and 2 in the blanks provided.

1. The following events are not listed in the order in which they are likely to occur. Number the events in chronological order from 1 to 5.

    _____ The monitor is made a residual claimant.

    _____ Increased shirking reduces the output of the firm.

    _____ Firm comes into existence.

    _____ A monitor is chosen.

    _____ People in the firm start to shirk.

2. A monitor may be made a residual claimant. How will this prevent the monitor from shirking?

    _____

    _____

Types of Firms

In questions 3–17, identify the type of firm (sole proprietorship, partnership, or corporation) that best answers the question.

3. Which type of firm has limited liability?

    _____

4. Which type of firm is likely to have the greatest number of owners?

    _____

5. Which types of firms have unlimited liability?

    _____

6. Which type of firm suffers from double taxation?

    _____

7. Which type of firm has only one owner?

    _____

8. Which type of firm is likely to have the shortest life span?

_____

9. Which type of firm is the easiest to form and to dissolve?

_____

10. Which type of firm is owned by stockholders?

_____

11. In which type of firm does a board of directors make the important decisions?

_____

12. In which type of firm is decision making often the easiest?

_____

13. Barbershops and restaurants are examples of which type of firm?

_____

14. Law firms and medical offices are examples of which type of firm?

_____

15. Wal-Mart, Best Buy, and General Electric are examples of which type of firm?

_____

16. Which type of firm accounts for the greatest number of firms?

_____

17. Which type of firm accounts for the greatest number of receipts (sales)?

_____

Double taxation is considered to be a disadvantage of corporations. Write your answers to questions 18–20 in the blanks provided.

18. Explain double taxation.

_____

_____

_____

19. Is it fair to tax corporate profits twice?

_____

_____

20. Some people argue that either the corporate income tax or the tax on dividends should be reduced or eliminated. What might be some of the effects of reducing or eliminating one or both of these taxes? (*Hint:* Consider the circular flow diagram of economic activity in the U.S. economy—Exhibit 3-2 on page 66 of your text.)

_____

_____

_____

_____

_____

Corporations, like all firms, can raise money by borrowing from banks and other lending institutions. However, corporations also can raise money by selling bonds or issuing additional shares of stock.

In questions 21–24, identify the type of financing (stock or bond) that best answers the question.

21. In which form of corporate financing is the investor a lender to the corporation?

_____

22. In which form of corporate financing is the investor also an owner? _____

23. Which form of corporate financing involves more risk for the investor? _____

24. Which form of corporate financing involves the potential for greater returns for the investor?

_____

Franchises

Write your answers to questions 25–27 in the blanks provided.

25. Franchises have become more common in the last 25 years. What are the advantages and disadvantages of buying a franchise?

Advantages:

_____

_____

Disadvantages:

_____

_____

26. According to Milton Friedman, what is the only social responsibility of business?

_____

_____

_____

27. Do you agree or disagree with Milton Friedman's opposition to businesses donating funds to charitable organizations? Give reasons for your answer.

_____

_____

_____

Apply what you have learned in this section by completing the following extension activities.

28. Present a Personal Anecdote Think of a time when you or someone else shirked their duties. This might have happened at work, at school, or during a fun activity such a camping trip. Make sure your story is not about anyone in your class, and change the names of the people involved. Prepare a short presentation telling what happened and expressing how you felt about it.

　　Present your personal anecdote, or story, to a small group of classmates. Listen carefully as the other group members present their anecdotes. Then, working as a group, discuss what general truths are implied by the various anecdotes. For instance, if someone tells a story about shivering through a camping trip because someone shirked the duty of collecting firewood, the implied general truth is that everyone suffers when one person decides to shirk.

29. Write an Editorial Reread the information in your book about Ralph Nader's and Milton Friedman's views of businesses' ethical and social responsibilities. Use your prior knowledge and experiences to decide whose view you agree with and then write a newspaper editorial that makes the case for your view. You may want to do some additional online research to support your case. Be sure that you attribute ideas and information to their proper author. When you have finished writing, edit and revise your draft. Make sure that you have used the possessive case correctly.

30. Research Business Property Restrictions When a company decides where to locate its business, it must first investigate any government restrictions by which it would have to abide. These restrictions determine how a business uses and disposes of business property. One such example is a zoning law. Zoning laws determine where commercial buildings can be placed within a community and may restrict how a building is used. Using the Internet, research your local zoning laws and identify where businesses are able to build and if there are any additional restrictions or ordinances in your community that affect businesses. List the restrictions and evaluate whether the restrictions might encourage or discourage a new business. Support your views with logical reasoning.

CHAPTER 7, SECTIONS 2 AND 3

Costs and Revenue

Fill in the blanks in questions 1–6 to be sure you understand some important economic terms.

1. A fixed cost _____ no matter how many units of a good are produced.

2. An example of a fixed cost is _____.

3. A variable cost _____ with the number of units of a good produced.

4. An example of a variable cost is _____.

5. In economics, the word _____ means additional, so _____ is the cost of producing an additional unit of a good and _____ is the revenue from selling an additional unit of a good.

6. Every firm wants to maximize _____.

Complete the cost and revenue formulas in questions 7–12.

7. Total cost (TC) =

   _____

8. Average total cost (ATC) =

   _____

9. Marginal cost (MC) =

   _____

10. Total revenue (TR) =

   _____

11. Marginal revenue (MR) =

   _____

12. Profit (or loss) =

   _____

13. Use the formulas in questions 7–12 to fill in the missing numbers in the following table. For this firm, marginal revenue is the same as price.

Gadgets/ hour	Fixed cost	Variable cost	Total cost	Marginal cost	Marginal revenue	Total revenue	Profit or (loss)
0	$24	$ 0	$ 24	$ 0	$24	$ 0	($ 24)
1	$24	_____	$ 32	$ 8	$24	$ 24	_____
2	_____	$ 12	$ 36	_____	$24	_____	$ 12
3	$24	$ 15	_____	$ 3	$24	_____	$ 33
4	$24	_____	$ 44	_____	_____	$ 96	_____
5	$24	_____	$ 51	$ 7	$24	_____	$ 69
6	$24	$ 36	_____	_____	$24	$144	_____
7	_____	$ 48	_____	$12	_____	$168	_____
8	$24	_____	$ 87	_____	$24	_____	$105
9	$24	_____	$106	$19	$24	$216	_____
10	$24	$106	_____	$24	$24	_____	$110
11	$24	$136	_____	_____	_____	$264	_____
12	_____	$173	_____	$37	$24	_____	$ 91

Total Revenue and Marginal Revenue

Every firm must answer certain questions. One question is: How much should the firm produce? Fill in the blanks in question 14 to answer this question. Then use the table in question 13 to answer questions 15–17.

14. According to economists, a business should continue to produce additional units of its good until

_____ is equal to _____.

15. So, the firm in question 13 should produce _____ gadgets at current prices.

16. If the price (marginal revenue) of gadgets rises to $37, the firm should produce _____ gadgets.

17. If the price (marginal revenue) of gadgets drops to $15, the firm should produce _____ gadgets.

A firm also needs to decide how many workers to hire. To see how a firm makes this decision, you need to understand the law of diminishing marginal returns. Fill in the blanks in questions 18 and 19 with the correct answers.

18. According to the law of diminishing marginal returns, if additional units of one

_____, such as labor, are added to another _____ in fixed

supply, such as capital, eventually the additional output (produced as a result of hiring an additional

worker) will _____.

19. If a firm adds workers to increase production, more _____ must be added to minimize the effects of the law of diminishing marginal returns.

A firm decides how many workers to hire by looking at both the costs and the benefits of an additional worker. The benefits are the additional output produced as a result of hiring an additional worker and the revenue generated by that additional output (price of good produced × additional output). The costs are the additional wages paid to an additional worker.

Another cost that firms must consider before adding more workers is whether there is a need for a larger business property. There are costs and benefits to purchasing any property—personal or business. The costs of purchasing a business property (a store, a factory, a building) are obvious. They include the time and money required to actually purchase the property (including the price of the property, the fees for the attorney who is looking over the purchase agreement, and so on). Costs of using business property can include utility bills and taxes. The benefits of the property are largely viewed in terms of the profits that can be earned from owning and operating a business within the confines of the business property.

Based on the above information, answer questions 20–21.

20. According to economists, as long as the additional output produced by the additional worker

    multiplied by the price of the good is _____ than the wage you have to pay the

    worker, then hire the worker.

21. Fill in the missing numbers in the following table.

Number of workers	Quantity of output per hour	Additional output produced by hiring an additional worker	Additional revenue generated if the price of the good is $5
0	0	0	$ 0
1	4	4	$20
2	10	6	$30
3	17	_____	_____
4	23	_____	_____
5	28	_____	_____
6	31	_____	_____
7	32	_____	_____
8	31	_____	_____

Use the table in question 21 to answer questions 22 and 23.

22. The law of diminishing marginal returns sets in with the _____.

23. If the firm pays workers $14 an hour, it should hire _____.

Apply what you have learned in this section by completing the following extension activities.

24. **Apply Prior Knowledge** In a small group, share your background knowledge about revenue. When have you heard the word revenue? What do you know about it? Next, read aloud the Section 3 definitions of *marginal revenue* and *law of diminishing marginal returns*. Work together to rewrite the definitions in your own words.

25. **Identify Costs and Benefits** Write an essay that analyzes the cost and benefits to purchasing and using business property. What day-to-day costs are incurred from owning this type of property? How do firms benefit from purchasing and using their own property?

CHAPTER 8, SECTION 1

A Perfectly Competitive Market

In questions 1–4, list the characteristics of a perfectly competitive market.

1. _____

   _____

2. _____

   _____

3. _____

   _____

4. _____

   _____

The characteristics of a perfectly competitive market determine certain characteristics of the sellers in the market. Write your answers to questions 5–8 in the blanks provided.

5. A seller in a perfectly competitive market is a price taker. What is a price taker?

   _____

   _____

6. Why does a price taker take the equilibrium price? Why doesn't he or she sell for a price that is higher or lower than equilibrium?

   _____

   _____

   _____

   _____

   _____

7. How much output does a seller in a perfectly competitive market produce?

   _____

   _____

8. What price does a seller in a perfectly competitive market charge for its product?

_____

_____

9. Fill in the missing numbers in the following table. The data are for a seller in a perfectly competitive market in which the equilibrium price is $15.

Units of output	Total revenue	Marginal revenue	Total cost	Marginal cost	Profit or (loss)
1	$ 15	$15	$21	—	($6)
2	$_____	$15	$29	$ 8	$ 1
3	$ 45	$_____	$33	$ 4	$12
4	$_____	$15	$37	$_____	$23
5	$ 75	$_____	$49	$12	$_____
6	$_____	$15	$64	$_____	$_____
7	$105	$_____	$81	$_____	$_____

Use the table in question 9 to answer questions 10 and 11.

10. How much output should the firm produce? _____

11. What price should the firm charge for its product? _____

Write your answers to questions 12–14 in the blanks provided.

12. In perfectly competitive markets, how does profit act as a signal?

_____

_____

13. What happens in a perfectly competitive market if the firms in the market earn profits?

_____

_____

_____

14. If a law is passed that taxes away the profits earned by firms in a perfectly competitive market, what might be the unintended effect of the tax?

_____

_____

_____

_____

_____

_____

CHAPTER 8, SECTION 2

A Monopolistic Market

Characteristics

In questions 1–3, list the characteristics of a monopolistic market.

1. _____
   _____

2. _____
   _____

3. _____
   _____

The characteristics of a monopolistic market determine certain characteristics of the seller in the market. Write your answers to questions 4–8 in the blanks provided.

4. Whereas a firm in a perfectly competitive market is a price taker, the firm in a monopolistic market is a
   _____.

5. For what price does a monopolist search?
   _____
   _____

6. How does a monopolist know when it has found the right price?
   _____
   _____

7. How much output does a monopolist produce?
   _____
   _____

8. What price does a monopolist charge for its product?
   _____

Price

Questions 9–11 relate to price in a monopolistic market. Write your answers in the blanks provided.

9. Is it easier for a perfectly competitive firm or for a monopolist to determine price? Explain.

   _____

   _____

10. Does a monopolist face any limit on the price it charges? Explain.

   _____

   _____

   _____

11. Is a monopolist guaranteed profits? Explain.

   _____

   _____

Types of Monopolies

Barriers to entry help maintain a monopolist's market position by protecting the monopolist from competition. For each of the barriers listed in questions 12–16, identify the type of monopoly—government or market—that results from the barrier. Then describe how the barrier limits competition.

12. public franchise

   Type of monopoly:

   _____

   Description:

   _____

   _____

13. extremely low average total costs

   Type of monopoly:

   _____

   Description:

   _____

   _____

14. patent

Type of monopoly:

_____

Description:

_____

15. copyright

Type of monopoly:

_____

Description:

_____

_____

16. exclusive ownership of a scarce resource

Type of monopoly:

_____

Description:

_____

_____

In each of questions 17–20, identify the company described as a government monopoly or a market monopoly.

17. Company A owns nearly all of the world's diamonds.

_____

18. Company B invents an entirely new product, and a patent is granted.

_____

19. Company C has the exclusive right to provide cable TV services to a city.

_____

20. Company D has per-unit costs that are much lower than those of any of its competitors.

_____

Laws

Each of the scenarios in questions 21–25 presents a monopoly issue. In each blank provided, write the name of the law that was passed to deal with the issue.

21. Company A, a nationally known "big box" store with 150,000 square feet of merchandise, builds a store in your city. Because company A buys from suppliers in huge quantities, it receives special discounts. The small businesses in town say they are unable to survive and must have protection from company A.

   _____

22. People in your town have been flocking to company W since it started its new advertising campaign. The company is making claims that seem too good to be true. The competitors of company W say that company W is using false advertising to deceive its customers.

   _____

23. Company X promises to sell a scarce resource to company B only if company B buys other goods from company X.

   _____

24. Company Y attempts to buy all the firms that compete with it.

   _____

25. Your chief competitor, company Z, slashes prices on its products. Its new prices are much lower than the prices charged by any of its competitors in town. You and the other business owners in town accuse company Z of cutthroat pricing.

   _____

Apply what you have learned in this section by completing the following extension activities.

26. **Present a TV Interview** View at least three different news reports about the investment scam run by Bernie Madoff that was discovered in late 2008. Take notes on what you learn. Next, put the Madoff scam in context by reading Internet headlines and articles about other Wall Street scandals of the early 2000s. View the news reports again and take notes on anything you may have missed the first time.

   With a partner, take turns playing the roles of TV interviewer and interviewee. The interviewer should ask, "How did the Madoff scam work?" After the interviewee has given a detailed response to this question, switch roles. The new interviewer should ask, "What damage was caused by Madoff's scam?" The new interviewee should answer at length, explaining all the consequences of the scam.

27. **Make Connections** Economic freedom is often linked to personal choice, voluntary exchange, and open markets. Although the U.S. free enterprise economic system is based on these economic goals of freedom, the government does enforce legislation to limit monopolies and to either limit or encourage competition. Legal barriers to entry (such as public franchises, copyrights, and patents) help to protect some businesses while restricting others and antitrust laws prohibit the creation of monopolies to promote fair competition. In an essay, analyze the costs and benefits of U.S. laws and legislation which restrict market activity and how they relate to the economic goals of freedom.

CHAPTER 8, SECTION 3

A Monopolistic Competitive Market

Characteristics

In questions 1–3, list the characteristics of a monopolistic competitive market.

1. _____
   _____

2. _____
   _____

3. _____
   _____

The characteristics of a monopolistic competitive market determine certain characteristics of the sellers in the market. Write your answers to questions 4 and 5 in the blanks provided.

4. How much output does a monopolistic competitor produce?

   _____
   _____

5. What price does a monopolistic competitor charge for its product?

   _____
   _____

Competition and Product

Questions 6 and 7 relate to the amount of competition a seller faces. Write your answers in the blanks provided.

6. Do most sellers prefer more competition or less competition? Explain why.

   _____
   _____

7. What two factors determine the amount of competition a seller faces?

_____

_____

Although two of the characteristics of monopolistic competition are the same as characteristics of perfect competition, unlike firms in perfectly competitive markets, monopolistic competitors sell slightly different products.

Write your answers to questions 8–10 in the blanks provided.

8. Some of the differences in monopolistic competitors' products are physical. What other kinds of differences might exist for products in this market?

_____

_____

9. Why does a monopolistic competitive firm try to differentiate its product from that of its competitors?

_____

_____

_____

_____

10. Most clothing producers are monopolistic competitors. When you go clothes shopping, what factors determine what jeans or shirts you buy? Do you see why firms try to differentiate their products?

_____

_____

_____

CHAPTER 8, SECTION 4

An Oligopolistic Market

Characteristics

In questions 1–3, list the conditions of an oligopolistic market.

1. _____

_____

2. _____

_____

3. _____

_____

The characteristics of an oligopolistic market determine certain characteristics and behavior of the sellers in the market. Write your answers to questions 4–7 in the blanks provided.

4. Is an oligopolist a price taker or a price searcher?

_____

5. How do economists identify oligopolistic industries?

_____

_____

_____

_____

6. Why might oligopolistic firms be tempted to enter into a cartel agreement?

_____

_____

7. Why do cartels usually fail?

_____

_____

_____

_____

Price Discrimination

Questions 8 and 9 concern price discrimination. Write your answers in the blanks provided.

8. Suppose you (age 17) go to the zoo with your little sister (age 5), your mother (age 42) and your grand-father (age 66). When you arrive at the zoo, you find the following sign at the admission stand.

Children (age 0–6)	$3
Students (age 6–18 with school ID)	$4
Senior Citizens (over 65)	$6
General Admission	$8

Your mother mumbles something about age discrimination under her breath. You ask what she means, and she explains that although she may enjoy the zoo the least, she is charged the most. She says, "Your little sister, who likely enjoys the zoo the most, is charged the least. What an unfair pricing system!" Having mastered your recent economics quiz on price discrimination, how would you explain the purpose of the zoo pricing structure?

_____

_____

_____

_____

_____

_____

_____

_____

_____

9. Stores often offer mail-in rebates for some of the products they sell. How are mail-in rebates a form of price discrimination?

_____

_____

_____

_____

_____

_____

_____

Apply what you have learned in this section by completing the following extension activities.

10. **Write A Historical Narrative** Look up the word *embargo* in a dictionary and then conduct Internet research to determine how embargoes are used in international politics. Use a graphic organizer, such as a diagram, to organize the information you find. When you feel you understand the concept of embargoes, research the OPEC oil embargo of 1973. Read at least two reliable sources of information on the topic. Based on your findings, write a historical narrative retelling the events that led up to the embargo, explaining who imposed the embargo and why, and summarizing the results of the embargo. When you have finished writing, edit and revise your narrative, paying special attention to correct pronoun use and pronoun agreement.

11. **Collaborate to Classify a Market** Working in a small group, collaborate to research the U.S. railroad industry just after the turn of the 20th century (the early 1900s). As part of your research, respond to the following questions: How many different railroad companies existed during this time period? How many different people or organizations owned them? Did people have a choice of which railroads to use?

    When you have finished your research, review the definitions of perfectly competitive, monopolistic, monopolistic competitive, and oligopolistic markets in your book. Work with your group to answer this question: Which kind of market was the railroad industry in the early 1900s, and how do you know? As a group, brainstorm to think of a current market of the same type. Compare and contrast it with the railroad industry of the early 1900s and then write a short report summarizing your findings.

CHAPTER 9, SECTION 1

What Determines Wages?

Wages In an Unskilled Labor Market

The following table shows the number of workers demanded and supplied at various wages in the unskilled labor market in H-Town. Use this table to respond to question 1.

UNSKILLED LABOR MARKET IN H-TOWN

Hourly wage	Number of workers	
	Demanded	Supplied
$4	14,000	2,000
$6	12,000	4,000
$8	10,000	6,000
$10	8,000	8,000
$12	6,000	10,000
$14	4,000	12,000
$16	2,000	14,000

1. Use the information in the table to draw the supply and demand curves for this labor market on the following grid. Use the wage rates (prices) and number of workers (quantities) demanded to plot the demand curve. Label it D_1. Use the wage rates and number of workers supplied to plot the supply curve. Label it S_1.

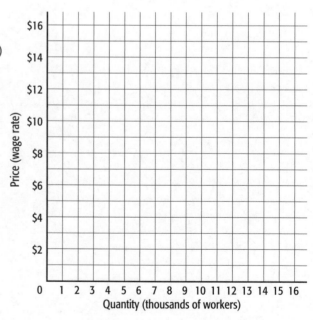

Unskilled Labor Market in H-Town

Use the graph you created in question 1 to answer questions 2 and 3.

2. The equilibrium wage for unskilled labor in H-Town is _____.

3. The equilibrium quantity for unskilled labor in H-Town is _____ workers.

Minimum Wage

Many community leaders make passionate speeches before the city council on behalf of the low-wage workers in H-Town. The community leaders maintain that the way to help low-wage workers is to raise the minimum wage. Due to the hard work and persuasive speeches, the city council of H-Town passes a law that sets the minimum wage at $15 an hour. Low-wage workers celebrate at the prospect of earning $15 an hour.

Use the above information to respond to question 4.

4. Illustrate the minimum wage by drawing a horizontal line at $15 on the graph you created in question 1.

Questions 5–10 are based on the new graph, which now shows a minimum wage of $15 an hour. Write your answers in the blanks provided.

5. The quantity demanded at the minimum wage is _____ workers.

6. The quantity supplied at the minimum wage is _____ workers.

7. The government of H-Town intended to help low-wage workers by setting the minimum wage at $15 an hour but, instead, has created a _____ of _____ workers.

8. Because these people are looking for work but cannot find it, they are considered _____.

9. Setting the minimum wage at $7.50 an hour had the _____ of creating an unemployment problem in H-Town.

10. Now, suppose that many of the citizens of H-Town want to get rid of the minimum wage of $15 an hour to try to reduce unemployment. In opposition, persuasive speakers paint a picture of workers earning only $3 an hour in the absence of government regulation. Explain why this scenario is highly unlikely.

_____

_____

_____

Write your answers to questions 11 and 12 in the blanks provided.

11. Who are the winners and who are the losers when the minimum wage is increased?

_____

_____

_____

12. Do you support an increase in the minimum wage? Why or why not?

_____

_____

Why Different Wages?

Questions 13–16 relate to the wages earned by different people. Write your answers in the blanks provided.

13. What are two of the reasons why some people earn more than others?

_____

_____

_____

14. Both doctors and sanitation workers may have a significant effect on people's health. Explain why doctors earn more than sanitation workers earn.

_____

_____

_____

15. Sally has just earned a degree in economics. She has two job offers, one from a university for $70,000 a year and one from a Wall Street investment bank for $150,000 a year. Assume Sally chooses the university job. Complete the formula that applies to this situation.

Benefits in a job =

_____

16. How much are the nonmoney benefits of the university job worth to Sally?

_____

_____

Real Income

Real income is adjusted for inflation. This provides a way to compare the real value of wages earned in different years by stating all incomes in constant prices. Use a variation of the formula described in the textbook: Real income = (Nominal income /CPI) × 100.

Example: Fred earned an income of $28,000 in 1985, when CPI was 107.6. He earned $60,000 in 2010 when the CPI was 218.1. In which year was his real income higher?

Answer: In 1985 his real income was $26,022.30 ($28,000 / 107.6 × 100 = $26,022.30). In 2010 his real income was $27,510.32 ($60,000/218.1 × 100 = $27,510.32). His real income was higher in 2010.

Questions 17–19 relate to comparing real wages.

17. Your great-grandfather, grandfather, and father are arguing about incomes over dinner on Thanksgiving Day. Each claims to have had a tougher time supporting his family. Your great-grandfather earned $4,000 a year in 1940 when the CPI was 14.0; your grandfather earned $12,000 a year in 1970 when the CPI was 38.8; and your father earned $50,000 a year in 2004 when the CPI was 188.9. Rank your patriarchal line from highest to lowest according to real income. Include the real income value for each rounded to the penny.

Highest real income:

_____

Second highest real income:

_____

Lowest real income:

_____

18. Your Aunt Judy complains that although she continues to earn more money each year, she doesn't seem to have as much buying power as she used to have. Use the real income formula described above to fill in the missing numbers in the following table. Round your answers to the nearest whole penny.

Year	Aunt Judy's money wage	CPI (1982-84 = 100)	Aunt Judy's real income
1995	$35,000	152.4	_____
2000	$39,000	172.2	_____
2005	$43,000	195.3	_____
2010	$48,000	218.1	_____
2013	$49,000	223.1	_____

19. Is your Aunt Judy correct? Has her real income been decreasing over time?

   _____

Apply what you have learned in this section by completing the following extension activities.

20. **Present Visual Information** Research the average Consumer Price Index for each of the last five years. Use the information you obtain to make a line graph showing your results. Place the years on the x-axis and an appropriate range of CPI values on the y-axis. When plotting the graph, round the CPI for each year to the nearest whole number. Next, research the amount of the hourly minimum wage for the last five years. Create a similar line graph showing your results. Place the years on the x-axis and an appropriate range of wages on the y-axis. Based on your graphs, write down your conclusions about the buying power of minimum-wage workers over the last five years.

   Prepare to present your graphs and conclusions to the class. Practice by presenting the graphs to a classmate, making sure to use accessible, understandable language. If you can't think of an exact English word, use synonyms or circumlocution (describing) to communicate your meaning. Explain the information represented by each graph and tell what your graphs led you to conclude about the buying power of minimum-wage earners. After you have finished practicing, make your presentation to the entire class.

21. **Collaborate to Pick Players** Working with a small group of classmates, select a sport and imagine that you are the owners of a professional team. Use the Internet to research athletes and organize a group discussion on who you want to see on your team.

Keeping in mind that the top pick is not always the best pick, collaborate to determine who you want for the main positions on the team. If you disagree on your choice of players, demonstrate active listening skills by discussing the pros and cons of your selections and sharing any helpful information you have gathered. Express your own opinions and work to finalize your team. Once you have finished, share your final selections with other groups.

CHAPTER 9, SECTION 2

Labor and Government Regulation

One of the objectives of a labor union may be to obtain higher wages for its members.
Wages are largely determined by supply and demand in the labor market.

Write your answers to questions 1 and 2 in the blanks provided.

1. How do unions try to influence the demand for labor to achieve higher wages?

   _____

   _____

2. How do unions try to influence the supply of labor to achieve higher wages?

   _____

   _____

**Each of the graphs in questions 3 and 4 shows the supply of and demand for union workers
in a particular labor market. Label the axes and the demand and supply curves on the graph.
Then the event described occurs. Illustrate the shift in the supply curve or the demand curve as
a result of the event. Then fill in the blanks in the statements below the graph with the correct
answers. (*Note:* The level of employment refers to the number of union workers employed.)**

3. *Event:* The union increases demand for the good
   produced.

   The _____ curve shifts

   to the _____, the wage

   for union workers _____,

   and the level of employment

   _____.

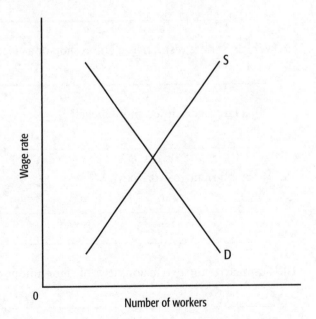

4. *Event:* The union decreases the supply of union workers.

The _____ curve shifts to the

_____, the wage for union

workers _____, and the level

of employment _____.

Write your answers to questions 5–13 in the blanks provided.

5. What is a closed shop?

_____

_____

6. What is a union shop?

_____

_____

7. Which is more restrictive, a union shop or a closed shop?

_____

8. What law made closed shops illegal?

_____

9. What is a right-to-work law?

_____

_____

10. Summarize the two major views of labor unions concerning their effects on production and efficiency.

_____

_____

_____

_____

11. Do you think labor unions are a beneficial aspect of the economy? Why or why not?

_____

_____

_____

12. The Latin phrase *caveat emptor* means "let the buyer beware." In practical terms, the phrase means that consumers are ultimately responsible for their buying decisions. Lately, government has tried to reduce the burden on consumers by regulating firms on behalf of consumers. Some people argue that the costs of regulation are too high. Other people say that consumers need the protection provided by regulation. List and discuss the costs and benefits of government regulation.

_____

_____

_____

_____

_____

13. Do you think there should be more or less government regulation? Give reasons for your answer.

_____

_____

_____

Apply what you have learned in this section by completing the following extension activities.

14. **Write a Speech** Find and read the Fair Labor Standards Act online. If you are having trouble understanding the language of the law, search for a reputable website that explains it. Make note of any unfamiliar words or language structures in the law. Look them up on the Internet or ask your teacher or a classmate to explain them to you. Finally, go back and re-read the law to confirm your understanding.

    Imagine that Congress is considering repealing the Fair Labor Standards Act. Predict what you think would happen if the law were repealed. Take notes about the effect on employers, employees, and the economy. Next, imagine that you work for a congressperson. Write a short speech for him or her to present in Congress either supporting or opposing the repeal of the Fair Labor Standards Act.

15. **Research Government Regulations** Select two different types of businesses in your community and identify local ordinances and regulations that apply to the establishment and operation of each. Begin your search on the city or county website. There you should be able to find information on business regulations, restrictions, and other ordinances. After your research, evaluate whether one business is more regulated than the other and if you agree or disagree with those regulations. Support your views with logical reasoning.

CHAPTER 10, SECTION 1

The Origins of Money

The Functions of Money

In questions 1–3, list and define the three functions of money, and then provide an example of how dollars fulfill that function. Write your answers on the lines provided.

1. *Function:*

   _____

   Definition:

   _____

   _____

   Example:

   _____

   _____

2. *Function:*

   _____

   Definition:

   _____

   _____

   Example:

   _____

   _____

3. *Function:*

   _____

   Definition:

   _____

   _____

   Example:

   _____

To be used effectively as a medium of exchange, money needs to be easy to carry. And to be used effectively as a unit of account, money needs to be easily divisible into various equivalent units. For example, a dollar is easily divided into 100 equivalent units (pennies).

The items in questions 4–9 have all been used as money at one time. Analyze each item in terms of how well it functions as money, by explaining whether or not the item fulfills the functions of money. Write your answers on the lines provided.

EXAMPLE

$5 bill

Medium of exchange: <u>A $5 bill is easy to carry and functions well as a medium of exchange.</u>

Unit of account: <u>A $5 bill is easily divided into equivalent units and functions well as a unit of account.</u>

Store of value: <u>A $5 bill holds value over time and functions well as a store of value.</u>

4. large stone wheel

Medium of exchange:

_____

_____

Unit of account:

_____

_____

Store of value:

_____

_____

5. seashells

Medium of exchange:

_____

_____

Unit of account:

_____

_____

Store of value:

_____

_____

6. cattle

Medium of exchange:

_____

_____

Unit of account:

_____

_____

Store of value:

_____

_____

7. bread

Medium of exchange:

_____

_____

Unit of account:

_____

_____

Store of value:

_____

_____

8. gold

Medium of exchange:

_____

_____

Unit of account:

_____

_____

Store of value:

_____

_____

9. cigarettes

Medium of exchange:

_____

_____

Unit of account:

_____

_____

Store of value:

_____

_____

From a Barter Economy to a Money Economy

Write your answers to questions 10 and 11 on the lines provided.

10. What are the disadvantages of living in a barter economy?

_____

_____

_____

_____

_____

_____

11. How did goldsmiths increase the money supply?

_____

_____

_____

_____

_____

_____

_____

_____

Apply what you have learned in this section by completing the following extension activities.

12. **Collaborate to Learn About the Past** Work with a small group to learn about the historical use of cowrie shells as money. Use the Internet and the library to find out when and where they were used, taking detailed notes. Be careful to evaluate your sources to make sure they are reliable.

    When you have completed your research, collaborate to make a map on poster board showing all of the countries or regions in which cowries shells were used as money and noting the time periods when this occurred. Work together to present and explain your map to the class. Have each group member tell about one part of the map.

13. **Research an Economic Term** The student text describes both *commodity money* and *fiat money*. Another term that is used to describe a type of money is *representative money*. This term is defined differently by different people. Some use this term to only identify a claim on a commodity money (such as a document that represents or "stands in place of" actual gold). Others use this term to denote any money where the face value of the money (the $5 or $10, say, written on the face (front) of the money) *represents* a greater value than the value of the material. Go online and find examples of people using this term. Then, using your research to support your view, describe representative money in your own words.

CHAPTER 10, SECTION 2
The Money Supply

The Components of the Money Supply

Write your answers to questions 1–5 on the lines provided.

1. The money supply can be expressed as the following equation: M1 = _____
   + _____ + _____.

2. As of February 2017, the largest part of the money supply was _____.

3. In February 2017, the money supply equaled _____.

4. Which is the larger measure of the money supply: M1 or M2? Explain.

   _____

   _____

5. Why aren't credit cards considered money?

   _____

   _____

Borrowing, Lending, and Interest Rates

Interest rates are determined by supply and demand in the loanable funds market. Fill in the blanks in questions 6–8 with the correct answers.

6. In the loanable funds market, the demanders of loans are called _____. They are the people in the economy who wish to obtain funds in order to buy goods or services.

7. In the loanable funds market, the suppliers of loans are called _____. They are the people in the economy who have funds that they want to lend.

8. In the loanable funds market, the price is the _____. It is the price demanders must pay to obtain a loan and the price suppliers will accept to offer a loan.

In each of questions 9–12, an event has occurred that will affect demand or supply in the loanable funds market. On the graph, illustrate the shift in the supply curve or the demand curve as a result of the event. Then fill in the blanks in the statement below the graph with the correct answers.

9. The demand for loans rises.

The _____ curve shifts to

the _____ and the interest

rate _____.

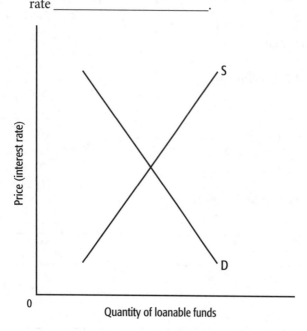

Quantity of loanable funds

10. The demand for loans falls.

The _____ curve shifts to

the _____ and the interest

rate _____.

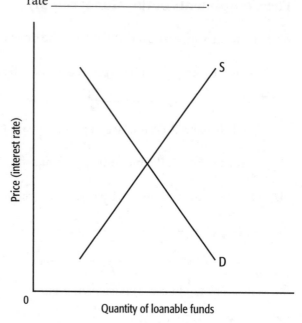

Quantity of loanable funds

11. The supply of loans rises.

The _____ curve shifts to

the _____ and the interest

rate _____.

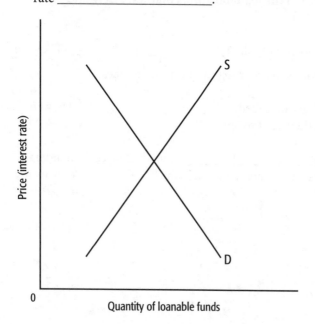

Quantity of loanable funds

12. The supply of loans falls.

The _____ curve shifts to

the _____ and the interest

rate _____.

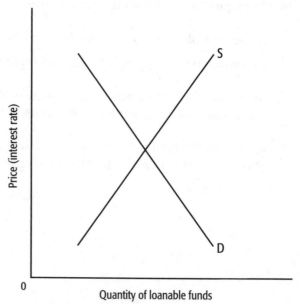

Quantity of loanable funds

Write your answers to questions 13–16 on the lines provided.

13. What happens if the demand for loans rises?

_____

_____

14. What happens if the demand for loans falls?

_____

_____

15. What happens if the supply of loans rises?

_____

_____

16. What happens if the supply of loans falls?

_____

_____

Name: _____   Date: _____

CHAPTER 10, SECTION 3

The Federal Reserve System

The Principal Components of the Fed

Write your answers to questions 1–4 on the lines provided.

1. What is the purpose of the Board of Governors of the Federal Reserve System?

   _____

2. What is the structure of the Board of Governors of the Federal Reserve System?

   _____

   _____

3. What is the FOMC?

   _____

   _____

4. What is the structure of the FOMC?

   _____

   _____

The Major Responsibilities of the Fed

In questions 5–10, list the major responsibilities of the Fed.

5. _____

6. _____

7. _____

8. _____

9. _____

10. _____

Write your answers to questions 11–13 on the lines provided.

11. What government agency prints paper money and how does it reach the public?

_____

_____

_____

_____

12. What is a reserve account?

_____

_____

13. Suppose Olivia writes a check payable to Matt and gives it to him. What happens to the check?

_____

_____

_____

_____

_____

_____

Effective Communication

Economic information should always be presented clearly and accurately. Poorly
communicated information creates confusion. When presenting information in written
form, care must be given to ensure that the information uses standard grammar,
spelling, punctuation, and sentence structure. If information is presented orally,
standard grammar and sentence structure should be used.

Apply what you have learned in this section by completing the following extension activities.

14. **Present a Response to a Speech** Find and view a video of a recent speech by the chairperson of
the Federal Reserve. As you watch, keep in mind that the language structures of oral speech may be
slightly different from those of written text. Find a transcript of the speech and read along as you listen
to the video a second time. Underline any unfamiliar words or language structures and ask a peer or
your teacher to explain them to you.

    Think about whether you agree with the chairperson's ideas about the economy and then present
an oral response to the speech to a partner. Express your opinion about the chairperson's ideas and
give reasons for your opinion. Listen to your partner's oral response and ask questions to clarify your
understanding. Be sure to use proper grammar and sentence structure while speaking.

15. **Write for a Website** Imagine that you are in charge of writing the Frequently Asked Questions (FAQ) page of the Federal Reserve website. One such question is "Why are U.S. banks required to keep reserves?" With a partner, research the answer to this question using your text and online sources. Read silently, pausing after each paragraph to ask your partner questions about any text you don't understand. If neither you nor your partner understand the text, ask your teacher for support.

Working on your own, write a short response to the question "Why are U.S. banks are required to keep reserves?" to be included on the Federal Reserve's FAQ page. With your partner, meet with another partner pair and have each person present their FAQ response out loud. Discuss which response answers the question best. If necessary, combine or edit the response until the group agrees.

Next, join another group of students and share your selected response with the other group. Discuss which response best answers the question. Continue combining groups and discussing the responses until your entire class has combined and has identified the best response to this question. Be sure that the written information uses standard punctuation, spelling, grammar, and sentence structures.

CHAPTER 10, SECTION 4

The Money Creation Process

Types of Reserves

Complete the formulas in questions 1–4.

1. Total reserves =

   _____

2. Required reserves =

   _____

3. Excess reserves =

   _____

4. Change in money supply =

   _____

How Banks Increase the Money Supply

Use the formulas from questions 1–4 to answer question 5.

5. Assume an initial deposit of $1,000 and that all money lent out by one bank is deposited in another bank. (Assume a 10% reserve requirement.)

   If a new checkable deposit of $1,000 is made in Bank A:

   - Required Reserves = _____

   - Excess Reserves = _____

6. What can Bank A do with its excess reserves?

   _____

7. Samantha takes a loan from Bank A equal to its excess reserves to buy a computer. The owner of the computer store deposits Samantha's money in Bank B.

   - Required Reserves = _____

   - Excess Reserves = _____

8. What can Bank B do with its excess reserves?

_____

9. Sam takes a loan from Bank B equal to its excess reserves to buy a TV. The owner of the electronics store deposits Sam's money in Bank C.

   • Required Reserves = _____

   • Excess Reserves = _____

10. What can Bank C do with its excess reserves?

_____

11. How much money could Bank C lend (excess reserves)? _____

12. Use your results to fill in the chart below.

Bank	New Checkable Deposits	Required Reserves (10%)	Loans
A	$1,000	$100	$900
B			
C			
Total			

13. The loans represent money created by the banking system. How much money was created by the banking system after these transactions? _____

14. Is your answer for question 13 the total amount that could be created with the initial $1,000 deposit?

_____

_____

Use the formula below to estimate the total change in the money supply.

Change in money supply = 1/Reserve Requirement × Change in reserves at first bank

15. What is the change in the money supply for an initial deposit of $1,000 if the reserve requirement is 5 percent (.05)?

_____

_____

16. What is the change in the money supply for an initial deposit of $1,000 if the reserve requirement is 10 percent (.10)?

_____

_____

17. What is the change in the money supply for an initial deposit of $1,000 if the reserve requirement is 15 percent (.15)?

_____

_____

18. Describe how changing the reserve requirement changes the money supply.

_____

_____

_____

_____

CHAPTER 10, SECTION 5

Fed Tools for Changing the Money Supply

Definitions of Terms

To be sure you understand some important economic terms, fill in the blanks in questions 1–3.

1. The buying and selling of government securities by the Fed is _____.

2. If a bank borrows money from the Fed, the interest rate charged by the Fed is called the

   _____.

3. If a bank borrows money from another bank rather than from the Fed, the interest rate charged by the
   second bank is called the _____.

Open Market Operations and the Discount Rate

Write your answers to questions 4–6 on the lines provided.

4. What difference does it make if a bank borrows from another bank (paying the federal funds rate) or
   from the Fed (paying the discount rate)?

   _____

   _____

5. Where does the Fed get the money to make an open market purchase?

   _____

   _____

6. What happens to the money the Fed receives from an open market sale?

   _____

   _____

Increasing or Decreasing the Money Supply

Complete the table in question 7.

7. The Fed has three tools it can use to influence the money supply. In the following table, list the three tools and then explain how the Fed uses each tool to increase or decrease the money supply.

Fed tool	To increase the money supply, the Fed	To decrease the money supply, the Fed

Name: _____   Date: _____

CHAPTER 11, SECTION 1

National Income Accounting

Determine whether or not the value of the good or service in each of the transactions in
questions 1–14 is included in the calculation of this year's U.S. GDP. If the value of the good
or service is not included, explain why not. Also note when the value of the good or service
is included in GNP but not in GDP.

1. Mycah buys a new bicycle that was produced in Detroit.

   _____

   _____

2. Kate cashes her social security check.

   _____

   _____

3. John buys a used refrigerator that was produced in Cleveland.

   _____

   _____

4. Melissa buys a new Hyundai car that was produced in South Korea.

   _____

   _____

5. Bryan buys a new Hyundai car that was produced in Alabama.

   _____

   _____

6. Elizabeth, an American citizen, owns and operates a coffee shop in Mexico.

   _____

   _____

7. Don owns and operates an accounting firm in Minnesota.

   _____

   _____

8. Stacy paints her parents' house.

_____

_____

9. Goodyear sells auto tires produced in Akron to General Motors for use on new GM cars.

_____

_____

10. Dianne buys stock in Starbucks.

_____

_____

11. Travis receives cash for repairing a neighbor's lawnmower.

_____

_____

12. Bruce buys a bootlegged DVD from a man on the street.

_____

_____

13. Dawn prepares a new area of her yard for a vegetable garden.

_____

_____

14. Jonah buys a new dishwasher for his house. The dishwasher was produced in Texas.

_____

_____

Apply what you have learned in this section by completing the following extension activity.

15. Write a Budget Imagine that you were living on your own. How much would you spend every month for housing, food, clothing, and transportation? Research the monthly cost of each of these items on the Internet and by checking prices at a grocery store. Take notes on your findings and then use them to write a monthly budget listing each of the items you researched. Add $25 a month for entertainment and then add up your total monthly expenses.

   Find a partner and compare your monthly budgets. Discuss any differences between them. Together, decide how much money you would need to make in order to live on your own.

CHAPTER 11, SECTION 2

Measuring GDP

Economists use the equation GDP = C + I + G + EX + IM to calculate gross domestic product (GDP). In questions 1–5, state what category of spending each variable in the equation stands for and then describe what is included in each category.

1. C stands for

   _____

   _____

2. I stands for

   _____

   _____

3. G stands for

   _____

   _____

4. EX stands for

   _____

   _____

5. IM stands for

   _____

   _____

In questions 6–15, identify the category into which the transaction should be placed by writing C, I, G, EX, or IM in the space provided. If the value of the good or service in the transaction is not included in GDP, indicate this by writing "not GDP" in the space.

6. _____ The U.S. government spends $5 billion to improve highways.

7. _____ Todd buys a new washing machine for his home.

8. _____ Judy buys a new computer for her engineering firm.

9. _____ Pfizer sells pharmaceuticals to a company in Germany.

10. _____ Bruce buys a Honda that was made in Japan.

11. _____ General Electric spends $10 million to build a new factory in New York.

12. _____ Mei-Ling buys stock in Google.

13. _____ The U.S. government pays your grandfather $500 as part of his social security entitlement.

14. _____ Melissa pays her hair stylist $50 for a haircut.

15. _____ Widgets, Inc., buys new vans to update its aging fleet of delivery vehicles.

In questions 16–19, identify the spending component of GDP (C, I, G, EX, or IM) that will be affected by the event described. Then state whether GDP will rise or fall due to the event, assuming no other spending component of GDP changes.

16. Foreign consumers choose to buy American cars.

    Spending component: _____   GDP will _____.

17. Business spending on factories and equipment increases.

    Spending component: _____   GDP will _____.

18. Congress passes a bill that includes a large amount of money earmarked for education.

    Spending component: _____   GDP will _____.

19. Consumers go on spending sprees all across the country, buying goods with the *Made in the USA* label.

    Spending component: _____   GDP will _____.

Per capita GDP is one measure of the standard of living in a country. In questions 20–22, calculate the per capita GDP rounded to the nearest dollar.

20. Country A has a population of 486,000 and a GDP of $27 billion. Per capita GDP is

    _____.

21. Country B has a population of 127 million and a GDP of $3.745 trillion. Per capita GDP is

    _____.

22. Country C has a population of 4.5 million and a GDP of $183 billion. Per capita GDP is

    _____.

23. Complete the following table to compare the countries in questions 20–22.

	GDP	Per capita GDP
Country with highest	_____	_____
Country with second highest	_____	_____
Country with lowest	_____	_____

24. Are the people in the country that has the highest per capita GDP in question 23 better off? Explain your answer.

    _____

    _____

    _____

CHAPTER 11, SECTION 3
Real GDP

Write your answers to questions 1 and 2 in the blanks provided.

1. Why do economists want to know real GDP?

   _____

   _____

   _____

2. Assume you live in an economy that only produces basketballs. Fill in the missing numbers in the following table. Remember that real GDP is equal to price in the base year times quantity in the current year. Use the year 2008 as the base year.

Year	Price of basketballs	Quantity of basketballs produced	GDP	Real GDP
2008	$25	15,000	_____	_____
2010	$27	13,000	_____	_____
2012	$29	16,000	_____	_____
2014	$32	15,000	_____	_____

Use the table in question 2 to answer questions 3–7.

3. In what year was GDP highest? _____

4. In what year was real GDP highest? _____

5. In what year did GDP rise, but real GDP fall? _____

6. What is true about GDP and real GDP in the base year? Explain.

   _____

   _____

   _____

7. Since GDP indicates a change in output that includes both price and quantity, while Real GDP is adjusted for inflation, what can you say about the period during which GDP increased, but real GDP decreased?

   _____

   _____

   _____

CHAPTER 11, SECTION 4

Measuring Price Changes and the Unemployment Rate

Write your answers to questions 1 and 2 in the blanks provided.

1. What is a price index?

   _____

2. What is the consumer price index (CPI)?

   _____

In questions 3–5, complete the formulas that relate to price and the CPI.

3. Percentage change in price =

   _____

4. $CPI_{current\ year}$ =

   _____

5. Percentage change in CPI =

   _____

The formulas in questions 3–5 are used in questions 6–20. Write your answers to questions 6–8 in the blanks provided.

6. Your favorite lunch is a hamburger and fries at the local Burger Barn. Last year, your favorite lunch was $5.95. This year, the same meal is $6.55. What was the percentage change in price?

   _____

7. In 1993, the average price of a new car was $12,750. In 2013, the average price of a new car was $31,252. What is the percent change in price of new cars from 1993 to 2013?

   _____

8. In January 1993, the median sale price of new homes was $118,000. In January 2013, the median sale price of new homes was $251,500. What is the percent change in price of new homes from January 1993 to January 2013?

   _____

Assume the market basket includes only the goods shown in the following table. Use formulas you used for answers to questions 4 and 5, and the table below to answer questions 9–13.

Good	Quantity	Price in base year	Price in current year
Pepperoni Pizza	15	$15.00	$17.50
Bottles of Soda	30	$ 1.25	$ 1.50
DVDs	10	$17.00	$19.00

9. The total amount spent on goods in the market basket in the base year was _____.

10. The total amount spent on goods in the market basket in the current year was _____.

11. The CPI for the base year was _____.

12. The CPI for the current year is _____.

13. The percentage change in the CPI from the base year to the current year was _____.

In questions 14–18, calculate the percentage change in the CPI between the two years shown. Round your answers to the nearest tenth of a percent.

14. | Year | CPI | *Percentage change in CPI:* _____
    | 2000 | 168.8 |
    | 2005 | 190.7 |

15. | Year | CPI | *Percentage change in CPI:* _____
    | 1990 | 127.4 |
    | 1995 | 150.3 |

16. | Year | CPI | *Percentage change in CPI:* _____
    | 1980 | 77.8 |
    | 1985 | 105.5 |

17. | Year | CPI | *Percentage change in CPI:* _____
    | 1970 | 37.8 |
    | 1975 | 52.1 |

18. | Year | CPI | *Percentage change in CPI:* _____
    | 1930 | 17.1 |
    | 1935 | 13.6 |

Use your answers to questions 14–18 to answer questions 19 and 20.

19. Which five-year period had the largest increase in the CPI?

_____

20. What is unusual about the period from 1930 to 1935?

_____

_____

In questions 21–23, complete the formulas that relate to unemployment.

21. Civilian labor force =

_____

22. Unemployment rate =

_____

23. Employment rate =

_____

24. Use the formulas in questions 21–23 to fill in the missing numbers in the following table. Change decimal answers to percents and round to the nearest tenth of a percent.

Year	Noninstitutional adult civilian population	Employed	Unemployed	Civilian labor force	Unemployment rate	Employment rate
2002	15,000	8,178	522	_____	_____	_____
2006	15,250	8,000	_____	8,390	_____	_____
2010	15,750	_____	614	9,500	_____	_____
2014	16,000	9,400	_____	10,000	_____	_____

Apply what you have learned in this section by completing the following extension activity.

25. Present Your Conclusions Use the Internet to find the current overall unemployment rate for the U.S. Next, research the rate of unemployment for workers with different educational backgrounds, such as young adults without a high school diploma and those with a diploma.

Use graphs and other visual organizers to enhance and confirm your understanding. Compare and contrast the unemployment rates of the different groups and then draw conclusions about education and unemployment. Why do some groups have higher rates than others? Who finds it hardest to get a job? Who finds it easiest?

Make sure these conclusions are based on your research and not on opinion or assumption. Present your conclusions to the class, explaining them with contextual support found during your research. Work to use a variety of sentence types and connecting words in your presentation. If you have trouble conveying your meaning in English, ask for assistance from your teacher. When you have finished your presentation, ask for and respond to questions.

Name: _____   Date: _____

CHAPTER 12, SECTION 1

Inflation and Deflation

Fill in the blanks in questions 1 and 2 with the correct answers.

1. _____ is an increase in the price level, or average level of prices.

2. _____ is a decrease in the price level, or average level of prices.

In questions 3–6, calculate the percentage change in the CPI and then indicate whether inflation or deflation has occurred. Round answers to the nearest tenth of a percent.

3. In 1974, the CPI was 46.6, and in 1975, the CPI was 52.1.

   Percentage change in CPI: _____

   Inflation or deflation: _____

4. In 1949, the CPI was 24.0, and in 1950, the CPI was 23.5.

   Percentage change in CPI: _____

   Inflation or deflation: _____

5. In 1997, the CPI was 159.1, and in 1998, the CPI was 161.6.

   Percentage change in CPI: _____

   Inflation or deflation: _____

6. In 1930, the CPI was 17.1, and in 1931, the CPI was 15.9.

   Percentage change in CPI: _____

   Inflation or deflation: _____

Write your answers to questions 7–10 in the blanks provided.

7. According to the simple quantity theory of money, what causes inflation? Explain.

   _____

   _____

   _____

   _____

   _____

8. At first glance, deflation would seem to be a positive occurrence for an economy. Why is deflation often destructive to an economy?

_____

_____

_____

_____

_____

9. On January 1, Jennifer puts $1,000 in a savings account that earns 4 percent interest. The inflation rate for the year is 2 percent. On December 31, will Jennifer's purchasing power have increased or decreased? Justify your answer.

_____

_____

_____

_____

10. On January 1, Jerry puts $1,000 in a savings account that earns 4 percent interest. The inflation rate for the year is 6 percent. On December 31, will Jerry's purchasing power have increased or decreased? Justify your answer.

_____

_____

_____

_____

In each of questions 11–14, an event has occurred that will affect aggregate demand or aggregate supply. On the graph, illustrate the shift in the AD curve or the AS curve as a result of the event. Then fill in the blanks in the statement below the graph with the correct answers. (*Note:* Identify the inflation or deflation that occurs as demand-side or supply-side.)

11. The Fed increases the money supply.

The _____ curve shifts to the

_____, the price

level _____, and

_____ occurs.

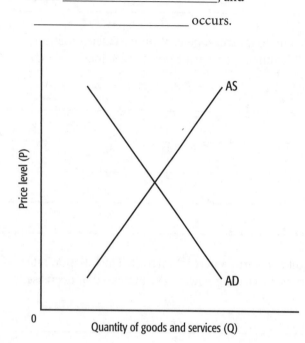

12. The Fed decreases the money supply.

The _____ curve shifts to the

_____, the price

level _____, and

_____ occurs.

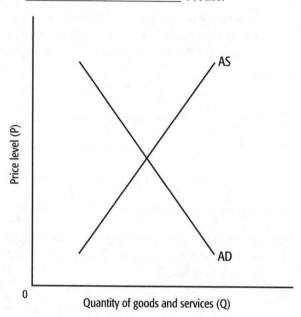

13. A drought destroys crops across the Midwest section of the United States.

The _____ curve shifts to the

_____, the price

level _____, and

_____ occurs.

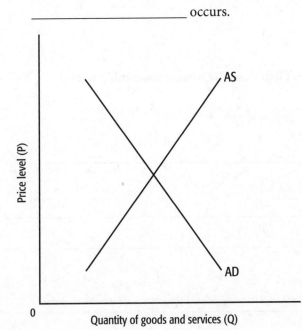

14. New technology makes it possible to produce more goods and services with existing resources.

The _____ curve shifts to the

_____, the price

level _____, and

_____ occurs.

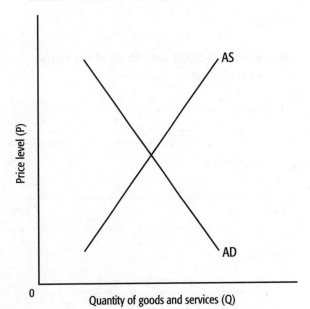

CHAPTER 12, SECTION 2

Business Cycles

Phases

In questions 1–5, list the phases of the business cycle. Then describe what is happening to real GDP in each phase.

1. *Phase:*

   _____

   Description:

   _____

   _____

2. *Phase:*

   _____

   Description:

   _____

   _____

3. *Phase:*

   _____

   Description:

   _____

   _____

4. *Phase:*

   _____

   Description:

   _____

   _____

5. *Phase:*

_____

Description:

_____

_____

Write your answers to questions 6–10 in the blanks provided.

6. What is the difference between a recession and a depression?

_____

_____

_____

7. In which phase of the business cycle do you think the economy would be most likely to experience inflation?

_____

_____

8. In which phase of the business cycle do you think the economy would be most likely to experience high unemployment?

_____

_____

9. Which type of economic indicator would be most helpful in predicting a change in economic conditions?

_____

_____

10. What are some examples of the type of economic indicator you identified in question 9?

_____

_____

Causes

Different economists identify different causes of a business cycle. These causes may affect the expansion phase of the business cycle when real GDP is increasing, the contraction phase of the business cycle when real GDP is declining, or both the contraction and expansion phases.

Based on the above information, respond to question 11.

11. In the following table, list the causes of a business cycle that have been identified by various economists. Then describe how each cause is believed to lead to expansion or contraction.

Cause	How it leads to expansion	How it leads to contraction

Apply what you have learned in this section by completing the following extension activity.

12. Write a Report On the Internet, find and view videos about the Great Depression. Make sure to select videos from reputable sources. Before you watch the videos, consider your prior knowledge of the Great Depression and make a list of what you already know.

As you watch the videos, pay attention to the images you see to help enhance your background knowledge of this era of American History. Monitor your understanding, and if you have trouble understanding the words or phrases you hear, seek clarification from the website, your teacher, or a parent.

When you have finished watching the videos, meet with a partner or a small group to discuss what you learned about the lives of ordinary people during the Great Depression. Take notes and ask questions during the discussion.

CHAPTER 12, SECTION 3

Economic Growth

Write your answers to questions 1–4 in the blanks provided.

1. What is the difference between absolute real economic growth and per capita real economic growth?

   _____

   _____

   _____

2. Can real GDP increase and per capita real GDP decrease at the same time? Explain.

   _____

   _____

3. Would you rather live in a country with absolute real economic growth or in a country with per capita real economic growth? Explain.

   _____

   _____

4. How can economic growth be achieved if an economy is currently producing at a point on its PPF?

   _____

   _____

Per capita real GDP is often used as a measure of standard of living. Use the Rule of 70 to answer questions 5–8.

5. If the annual growth rate of per capita real GDP is 1 percent, your standard of living will double in _____ years.

6. If the annual growth rate of per capita real GDP is 2 percent, your standard of living will double in _____ years.

7. If the annual growth rate of per capita real GDP is 5 percent, your standard of living will double in _____ years.

8. If the annual growth rate of per capita real GDP is 7 percent, your standard of living will double in _____ years.

In questions 9–14, list the factors that can cause economic growth by inducing a rightward shift in an economy's PPF. Then explain how each factor relates to economic growth.

9. *Factor:*

_____

   Explanation:

_____

_____

_____

10. *Factor:*

_____

   Explanation:

_____

_____

_____

11. *Factor:*

_____

   Explanation:

_____

_____

_____

12. *Factor:*

_____

   Explanation:

_____

_____

_____

13. *Factor:*

_____

   Explanation:

_____

_____

14. *Factor:*

_____

Explanation:

_____

_____

_____

Write your answers to questions 15–17 in the blanks provided.

15. If you could rule the United States for a day, what changes would you make to ensure future economic growth?

_____

_____

_____

_____

16. An ongoing debate in society involves whether or not more (or faster) economic growth is beneficial. Summarize the views of the two sides of this debate.

_____

_____

_____

_____

_____

_____

_____

17. Which side of the debate in question 16 do you support? Why?

_____

_____

_____

_____

_____

_____

Apply what you have learned in this section by completing the following extension activities.

18. **Present the Story Behind the Technology** Think of a new technology that interests you. Find articles on the Internet that tell how this technology was developed. Take notes about who worked on the technology, what skills they had, how long it took, and what problems were overcome during development. Include any other interesting information that you find about the technology.

    Write an outline for a presentation that describes how the technology you researched was developed. Practice giving your presentation in front of a classmate. Monitor your language as you speak, correcting any errors you make as you go. Be sure to use a variety of sentence types and include terms and phrases that your class would recognize from your economics text. When you are ready, give your presentation to the whole class.

19. **Collaborate to Create a Party Platform** Visit the official websites for the Republican and Democratic parties. With a small group, read the economic portions of the party platform on the websites. Take turns reading and pause frequently to relate what you have read to your prior experience with politics. Confirm your understanding by reading the party platform information again if necessary.

    Imagine that your group is forming its own political party. Collaborate to decide what economic ideas should be included in your party platform. Give your party a name and write a description of your economic platform. Post it in your classroom.

20. **Write an Informative Article** Imagine that you are a writer for the local newspaper. You have been asked to write an economic article about productivity and economic growth that the average reader would understand. Write a one-page informative article that analyzes and explains how productivity is related to economic growth. Be sure that your article uses standard punctuation and is free of all grammatical errors.

CHAPTER 13, SECTION 1

Fiscal Policy

Government uses fiscal policy to achieve particular economic goals. Fill in the blanks in questions 1–6 to be sure you understand fiscal policy.

1. If government increases _____, reduces _____, or both, government is said to be implementing expansionary fiscal policy.

2. If government decreases _____, raises _____, or both, government is said to be implementing contractionary fiscal policy.

3. According to some economists, government can use expansionary fiscal policy to reduce

   _____.

4. According to some economists, government can use contractionary fiscal policy to reduce

   _____.

5. Because high unemployment is most likely to occur during the _____ phase of the business cycle, government might consider using _____ fiscal policy at this time.

6. Because high inflation is most likely to occur during the _____ phase of the business cycle, government might consider using _____ fiscal policy at this time.

7. When government implements fiscal policy, it acts to change taxes, government spending, or both. Complete the following table by explaining for each type of fiscal policy how some economists believe changing taxes or government spending affects the economy.

	Expansionary fiscal policy	Contractionary fiscal policy
Taxes		
Government spending		

Use the following key to label each of the government actions in questions 8–12 as expansionary or contractionary fiscal policy.

E = expansionary fiscal policy
C = contractionary fiscal policy

8. _____ The government cuts income tax rates.

9. _____ The government eliminates most tax deductions and tax credits.

10. _____ The government increases spending for education.

11. _____ The government raises the social security tax rate.

12. _____ The government cuts funding to the NASA program.

For each of the economic problems described in questions 13–17, determine the type of fiscal policy that might be used to solve the problem. Then indicate whether taxes and government spending should be increased or decreased to implement the fiscal policy.

13. The economy is growing at a rapid pace and the inflation rate has hit 9 percent.

Type of fiscal policy:

_____

Taxes:

_____

Government spending:

_____

14. The unemployment rate hit 11 percent last month.

Type of fiscal policy:

_____

Taxes:

_____

Government spending:

_____

15. Corporations are recording record profits and the incomes of consumers are rising rapidly; economists worry that the economy may be growing too rapidly.

Type of fiscal policy:

_____

Taxes:

_____

Government spending:

_____

16. The stock market has been declining for several weeks, and surveys show that consumer confidence is at a four-year low. Economists worry that the economy may be slowing.

    Type of fiscal policy:

    _____

    Taxes:

    _____

    Government spending:

    _____

17. The economy has been lagging; real GDP reports have been negative for three consecutive quarters.

    Type of fiscal policy:

    _____

    Taxes:

    _____

    Government spending:

    _____

Write your answers to questions 18–20 in the blanks provided.

18. How might complete crowding out make expansionary fiscal policy ineffective?

    _____

    _____

    _____

    _____

19. According to Keynes, what was wrong with the classical school view of the economy?

    _____

    _____

    _____

    _____

20. According to supply-side economists, how can a reduction in personal income tax rates increase tax revenues?

    _____

    _____

    _____

    _____

Apply what you have learned in this section by completing the following extension activities.

21. **Write a Top-Three List** Research John Maynard Keynes' most important ideas, either at the library or on the Internet. Read silently and take careful notes. Decide which three ideas you think are most important and list them below. Compare your list with a classmate's list, explaining to him or her why you chose the ideas you did.

22. **Collaborate to Understand Suffixes** With a small group, take turns reading Section 1 of Chapter 13 aloud. If you encounter material you do not understand, ask your teacher for support. When you have finished, read the definitions of the words *expansionary* and *contractionary*. On the board or a piece of paper, write the words without their suffixes (*expansion* and *contraction*). Look up the suffix *–ary* to review its meaning. Finally, collaborate to think of at least five other words that use the suffix *–ary* and then compare and contrast the meanings of these words and the ways in which they are used.

CHAPTER 13, SECTION 2

Monetary Policy

The Federal Reserve uses monetary policy to achieve particular economic goals. Fill in the blanks in questions 1–6 to be sure you understand monetary policy.

1. If the Fed increases _____, it is said to be implementing _____ monetary policy.

2. If the Fed decreases _____, it is said to be implementing _____ monetary policy.

3. According to many economists, the Fed should use expansionary monetary policy to reduce _____.

4. According to many economists, the Fed should use contractionary monetary policy to reduce _____.

5. The Fed is most likely to use expansionary monetary policy during the _____ phase of the business cycle.

6. The Fed is most likely to use contractionary monetary policy during the _____ phase of the business cycle.

7. Recall that the Fed has three tools it can use to influence the money supply. Complete the following table by explaining how the Fed uses each tool to reduce unemployment or inflation.

Fed tool	To reduce the unemployment rate,	To reduce inflation,
Reserve requirement		
Open market operations		
Discount rate		

Some economists believe monetary policy should be implemented by using the exchange equation to achieve a stable price level. Write your answers to questions 8–12 in the blanks provided.

8. Complete the following version of the exchange equation: %∆M =

_____

9. If the average annual change in quantity is 4 percent, the average annual change in velocity is 2 percent, and the objective is to keep prices stable, then how should the Fed change the money supply?

_____

10. If the average annual change in quantity is 7 percent, the average annual change in velocity is 3 percent, and the objective is to keep prices stable, then how should the Fed change the money supply?

_____

11. If the average annual change in quantity is 2 percent, the average annual change in velocity is 4 percent, and the objective is to keep prices stable, then how should the Fed change the money supply?

_____

12. If the average annual change in quantity is 5 percent, the average annual change in velocity is 0 percent, and the objective is to keep prices stable, then how should the Fed change the money supply?

_____

CHAPTER 13, SECTION 3

Stagflation: The Two Problems Appear Together

Fill in the blanks in questions 1–3 with the correct answers.

1. Stagflation is the occurrence of _____ and _____ at the same time.

2. If the economy is experiencing stagflation and either fiscal or monetary expansionary policy is implemented, the _____ problem is likely to be solved but the _____ problem is likely to be made worse.

3. If the economy is experiencing stagflation and either fiscal or monetary contractionary policy is implemented, the _____ problem is likely to be solved but the _____ problem is likely to be made worse.

Economists disagree about the cause of stagflation. Some believe that an erratic monetary policy causes stagflation, while others believe a marked decrease in aggregate supply can also cause stagflation. Write your answers to questions 4–7 in the blanks provided.

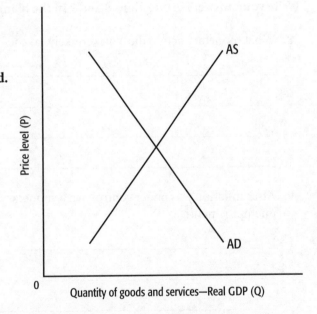

4. Suppose a sharp fall in the market supply of oil increases the costs of producing goods and services. As a result, aggregate supply decreases. On the graph above illustrate the shift in the AS curve.

5. As a result of the shift of the AS curve in question 4, the price level _____ and real GDP _____.

6. An increase in the price level is _____, and a decline in real GDP leads to a rise in _____. The result of the decrease in aggregate supply is _____.

7. How might an erratic monetary policy (a stop-and-go, on-and-off monetary policy) cause stagflation?

_____

_____

_____

_____

_____

_____

_____

In the stagflation of the 1970s, Paul Volcker, chairman of the Fed at the time, attacked inflation first, which caused a further increase in unemployment. After inflation was under control, Volcker worked to reduce unemployment. Although he is given much credit in hindsight, Volcker was among the most unpopular men in America at the time because of the unemployment that resulted as his policies took effect.

Write your answers to questions 8 and 9 in the blanks provided.

8. What monetary action did Volcker likely take to restrain inflation?

_____

_____

_____

_____

9. After inflation was under control, what monetary action did Volcker likely take to reduce unemployment?

_____

_____

_____

_____

Apply what you have learned in this section by completing the following extension activity.

10. **Present a Report** Conduct research to learn about the last time there was stagflation in the U.S. economy. Find out how stagflation affected people's lives and find photos that show these effects. Print out the photos and use them as visual support as you give a report to the class about what stagflation means for ordinary people. Make sure to use the photos you printed to support your presentation.

CHAPTER 14, SECTION 1

Taxes

1. Complete the following table with the information provided in the textbook.

Federal Tax	Revenue Raised in 2016	Percentage of total federal tax revenue in 2016
Personal Income Tax		
Corporate Income Tax		
Social Security Tax		

2. In 2016, the largest share of federal revenues came from the _____.

3. Complete the following table describing the three types of taxes.

Type of Tax	Description
Proportional Income Tax	
Progressive Income Tax	
Regressive Income Tax	

4. If your goal is to create a similar tax burden for people of all income levels, you would likely choose a _____ income tax.

5. If your goal is to make those with high incomes pay a greater share of the tax burden, you would most likely choose a _____ income tax.

6. Which type of tax does the United States use for its income tax? _____

7. According to Exhibit 14-6, in 2014 the top 50% of income earners earned _____ of total U.S. income, and paid _____ of federal income taxes.

8. According to Exhibit 14-6, in 2014 the bottom 50% of income earners earned _____ of total U.S. income, and paid _____ of federal income taxes.

9. After examining the information in this section, do you think the wealthy in the United States pay their "fair share" of federal taxes? Explain and provide evidence to support your answer.

Apply what you have learned in this section by completing the following extension activities.

10. **Research in Your Community** People pay taxes at the local, state, and national levels. State and local tax revenues support the needs of the state and local communities. Research and identify the types of local taxes paid in the city in which you live. Then, as a class, discuss the details of these taxes.

11. **Present Your Opinion** Using written and video resources, research what people are saying about the costs and benefits of implementing a flat income tax in the United States. Do you think a flat tax would be economically sound? Do you think it would be fair?

    Decide whether you support or oppose a flat income tax, and think of at least three reasons why. Write notes describing your reasons. Present your opinion and your reasons to the class. Make sure to use appropriate vocabulary words you have encountered in your research and in your Economics textbook. Monitor yourself as you speak and make any necessary corrections to your speech as you go.

12. **Write an Evaluation** Find a state or federal tax (other than a tax on soda) that has been implemented with the intention of changing people's behavior and then do research to evaluate how successful the tax has been. Find and read charts and graphs to aid comprehension and develop background knowledge. Take careful notes as you read silently.

    Imagine that you are a public servant in charge of evaluating this particular tax and reporting back to the lawmakers who imposed it. Write a report stating what you have found about the tax's success and making a recommendation to continue or repeal the tax.

13. **Collaborate to Learn Vocabulary in Context** Working with a partner, read the content about progressive income taxes in Section 1 of Chapter 14. When you are finished, collaborate to list meanings of the word *progressive* that are familiar to you. Finally, look up *progressive* in a dictionary. Break the word down into its root and affix. Using accessible language, write a definition of the word as it is used in your text.

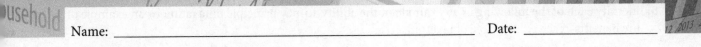

Name: _____   Date: _____

CHAPTER 14, SECTION 2

The Budget: Deficits and Debt

On the circles provided in questions 1 and 2, draw pie charts that show federal government tax revenue and federal government spending. (Use Chapter 14, Section 1 for government revenue data and Section 2 for government spending data.) Divide the circles and label the sections using the percentages in your text. (*Note:* Each circle will have a section labeled *Other.*)

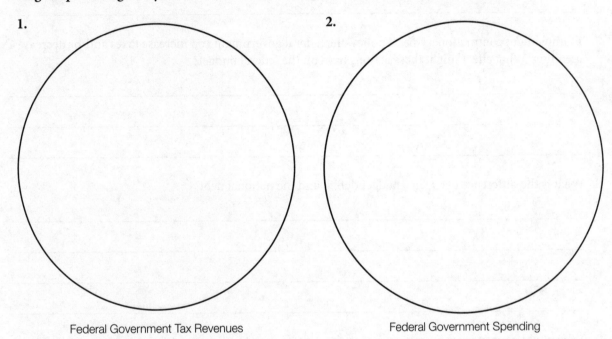

1.

2.

Federal Government Tax Revenues

Federal Government Spending

Write your answers to questions 3–10 in the blanks provided.

3. The following events are not listed in the order in which they occur. Number the events in chronological order from 1 to 4.

_____ The budget is presented to Congress.

_____ The full Congress votes and passes the budget.

_____ Congressional committees and subcommittees scrutinize the budget.

_____ The president of the United States prepares the budget.

4. What is the difference between the benefits-received and the ability-to-pay principles of taxation?

_____

_____

_____

_____

_____

5. Identify each of the following as an example of the ability-to-pay principle of taxation or an example of the benefits-received principle of taxation.

   a. The federal income tax structure is progressive. _____

   b. A state's automobile license fees finance highway maintenance. _____

6. To implement expansionary fiscal policy, the federal government can decrease taxes and/or increase spending. What effect might these actions have on the federal budget?

   _____

   _____

   _____

7. To implement contractionary fiscal policy, the federal government can increase taxes and/or decrease spending. What effect might these actions have on the federal budget?

   _____

   _____

   _____

8. What is the difference between a budget deficit and the national debt?

   _____

   _____

   _____

   _____

9. Why might your generation end up paying the debt incurred by the spending of your parents' generation?

   _____

   _____

   _____

10. Does what the government spends its revenue on matter to future generations?

   _____

   _____

   _____

   _____

CHAPTER 15, SECTION 1

International Trade

Terms

Fill in the blanks in questions 1–3 to be sure you understand some important economic terms that relate to trade.

1. When a country can produce more of a good than another country can produce with the same quantity of resources, the first country has a(n) _____ in the production of the good.

2. When a country _____ in the production of a good, it produces only that good.

3. When a country can produce a good at a lower opportunity cost than that of another country, the first country has a(n) _____ in the production of the good.

Opportunity Costs

Stacy and Travis both produce garden ornaments, including bamboo wind chimes and wooden birdhouses. Stacy and Travis make the wind chimes and birdhouses by assembling parts manufactured by other people. The following table shows the number of wind chimes and birdhouses that Stacy and Travis can make in one hour.

Use the table to answer questions 4–8.

	Wind chimes	Birdhouses
Stacy	3	1
Travis	2	3

4. When Stacy spends one hour making _____ wind chime(s), she gives up the opportunity to make _____ birdhouse(s). So for Stacy, the opportunity cost of making a wind chime is _____ birdhouse(s).

5. When Stacy spends one hour making _____ birdhouse(s), she gives up the opportunity to make _____ wind chime(s). So for Stacy, the opportunity cost of making a birdhouse is _____ wind chime(s).

6. When Travis spends one hour making _____ wind chime(s), he gives up the opportunity to make _____ birdhouse(s). So for Travis, the opportunity cost of making a wind chime is _____ birdhouse(s).

7. When Travis spends one hour making _____ birdhouse(s), he gives up the opportunity to make _____ wind chime(s). So for Travis, the opportunity cost of making a birdhouse is _____ wind chime(s).

8. Fill in the blanks to summarize Stacy's and Travis's opportunity costs for 1 wind chime (W) and 1 birdhouse (B).

Opportunity cost of 1 wind chime

Stacy: 1W = _____ B

Travis: 1W = _____ B

Opportunity cost of 1 birdhouse

Stacy: 1B = _____ W

Travis: 1B = _____ W

Comparative Advantage

Use the results you summarized in question 8 to answer questions 9–17.

9. Who has a comparative advantage in making wind chimes? Explain.

_____

_____

10. Who has a comparative advantage in making birdhouses? Explain.

_____

_____

11. Who should specialize in making wind chimes? Why?

_____

_____

12. Who should specialize in making birdhouses? Why?

_____

_____

13. If she doesn't specialize and spends one hour making wind chimes and one hour making birdhouses, Stacy makes _____ wind chime(s) and _____ birdhouse(s). If she specializes and spends both hours making wind chimes, Stacy makes _____ wind chime(s).

14. If he doesn't specialize and spends one hour making wind chimes and one hour making birdhouses, Travis makes _____ wind chime(s) and _____ birdhouse(s). If he specializes and spends both hours making birdhouses, Travis makes _____ birdhouse(s).

15. If Stacy and Travis do not specialize and each spends one hour making wind chimes and one hour making birdhouses, then together they produce _____ wind chimes and _____ birdhouses.

16. If Stacy and Travis specialize and spend two hours working in the area in which each has a comparative advantage, then together they produce _____ wind chimes and _____ birdhouses.

17. Suppose that a manufacturing firm decides to specialize in production. What might the results of such specialization be?

_____

_____

_____

Advantage and Specialization

Suppose two nations, Smithville and Jonesland, can produce wheat and rice. The following table shows the combinations of the two goods that each country can produce with the same amount of resources. Write your answers to questions 18–21 on the lines provided.

Smithville
Combination A: 90 wheat and 0 rice
Combination B: 60 wheat and 10 rice
Combination C: 30 wheat and 20 rice
Combination D: 0 wheat and 30 rice

Jonesland
Combination E: 15 wheat and 0 rice
Combination F: 10 wheat and 5 rice
Combination G: 5 wheat and 10 rice
Combination H: 0 wheat and 15 rice

18. Which country has an absolute advantage in producing wheat? Why?

_____

_____

19. Which country has an absolute advantage in producing rice? Why?

_____

_____

20. Which country has a comparative advantage in producing wheat? Explain.

_____

_____

21. Which country has a comparative advantage in producing rice? Explain.

_____

_____

When the two countries do not specialize or trade, Smithville produces and consumes combination B (60 wheat and 10 rice) and Jonesland produces and consumes combination F (10 wheat and 5 rice). Now suppose Smithville and Jonesland decide to specialize in the good in which each has a comparative advantage and agree to trade 20 units of wheat for 10 units of rice.

Write your answers to questions 22–24 on the lines provided.

22. What good should each country specialize in producing and how much of the good should it produce?

_____

_____

_____

23. Complete the following to show the amount of each good each country has after specializing and trading.

    Smithville: _____ wheat and _____ rice

    Jonesland: _____ wheat and _____ rice

24. Complete the following to show the benefits for each country of specialization and trade.

    Smithville: _____ more units of wheat and _____ more units of rice

    Jonesland: _____ more units of wheat and _____ more units of rice

Outsourcing and Offshoring

Write your answers to questions 25 and 26 on the lines provided.

25. What is the difference between outsourcing and offshoring?

_____

_____

_____

26. Why might politicians speak against offshoring but not mention the benefits of offshoring?

_____

_____

_____

_____

_____

_____

_____

_____

_____

Exports and Imports and their Impact

Recall that the balance of trade for any country (including the United States) is the difference between the value of its exports and the value of its imports. The imports and exports of a country have a direct impact on that country and its trading partners since the more a country imports the more likely it will have a balance of a trade deficit and the more it exports, the more the trade deficit will change from a deficit to a surplus.

Information Validation

Validating information found online or otherwise is necessary to make sure that the information is accurate and free of bias. You will be hard pressed to find economic articles, aside from dictionary entries, that don't contain some level of the author's own perspective. Validating information requires critical thinking skills.

First, determine if the source is a primary source or a secondary source. *Primary sources* are original and unedited materials created by someone who was directly involved (such as diaries, interviews, speeches, and so on). *Secondary sources* contain commentary or analysis of ideas, events, and primary sources.

Second, identify who created the content and whether that group or individual has a specific bias, point of view, or frame of reference that could distort information in any way. These describe ideas, assumptions, and perspectives that determine how information will be approached, interpreted, and presented. Although various opinions and perspectives are welcome in a free economy, propaganda (that is, false or exaggerated information) is not. Always validate the information in your sources, always attribute ideas to their authors, and never use unreliable or inaccurate data when presenting information to others.

Apply what you have learned in this section by completing the following extension activities.

27. **Present an Export Report** Research the main U.S. exports. Answer the question, "In which goods does the U.S. specialize?" Choose one of the exports and research how much of it the U.S. exports and to which countries. Create a graphic organizer that presents this information. Next, search the Internet to find out what experts are saying about the future of this export. Do they believe we will export more or less of these goods in the future?

    Present a report to the class about this export that refers to your graphic organizer and utilizes key words and expressions learned in class. Include a forecast for the future.

28. **Analyze and Evaluate Information** Find two articles related to outsourcing jobs (either outsourcing or offshoring). Find one article that is in favor of outsourcing jobs and another that is against the practice. Once you have found these sources, analyze the validity of the content by evaluating the source and the author of the article. Is it a primary or secondary source? Who is the author of the article? What can you find out about the author? Is there any evidence that the author has a particular bias, frame of reference, or perspective? Finally, evaluate whether you would consider the information and its source to be a reliable source of information. Support your view with evidence from your analysis.

29. **Analyze Trading Relationships** Analyze the following scenarios and identify the impact to the country/countries involved.

    Scenario 1 The U.S. begins to import more foreign-produced goods.

    _____

    Scenario 2 The U.S. begins to export more goods.

    _____

    Scenario 3 The U.S. buys more goods from Mexico.

    _____

    Scenario 4 The U.S. sells more goods to Germany.

    _____

CHAPTER 15, SECTION 2

Trade Restrictions

Tariffs and Quotas

The two major trade restrictions are tariffs and quotas. Tariffs and quotas, as noted in your book, benefit domestic producers and are arguably an inefficient U.S. policy. In economics, efficiency is achieved when net benefits have been maximized. This means that a U.S. policy is only efficient if the benefits of the policy are greater than the costs. Economists almost all agree that the benefits of tariffs and quotas to domestic producers of goods that compete with the imported goods are far less than the costs of the tariffs and quotas, tariffs and quotas are often placed on foreign imports. In short, sometimes U.S. policies (tariffs and quotas being one example) would be considered economically inefficient.

Write your answers to questions 1–7 in the blanks provided.

1. What is a tariff?

   _____

2. Who benefits from a tariff?

   _____

3. What is the effect of a tariff on consumers?

   _____

4. What is a quota?

   _____

5. Who benefits from a quota?

   _____

6. What is the effect of a quota on consumers?

   _____

7. Why is government often more responsive to producer interests than to consumer interests?

   _____

   _____

   _____

   _____

Arguments for Trade Restrictions

Arguments have been advanced for trade restrictions. For questions 8–12, list and explain the arguments in favor of trade restrictions. Then explain the criticism of each argument.

8. *Argument:*

   _____

   Explanation:

   _____

   _____

   _____

   Criticism:

   _____

   _____

   _____

   _____

9. *Argument:*

   _____

   Explanation:

   _____

   _____

   _____

   Criticism:

   _____

   _____

   _____

   _____

10. *Argument:*

    _____

    Explanation:

    _____

    _____

    _____

    Criticism:

    _____

    _____

    _____

11. *Argument:*

_____

Explanation:

_____

_____

_____

Criticism:

_____

_____

_____

12. *Argument:*

_____

Explanation:

_____

_____

Criticism:

_____

_____

_____

Organizations

In questions 13–18, identify the full name of each organization and briefly describe its function.

13. EU

_____

_____

14. NAFTA

_____

_____

15. CAFTA-DR

_____

_____

_____

16. WTO

_____

_____

17. IMF

_____

_____

_____

18. IBRD

_____

_____

_____

Apply what you have learned in this section by completing the following extension activities.

19. **Collaborate to Measure Quality of Life** Work with a small group to learn about The Economist Intelligence Unit's quality-of-life index. Start by looking up the expression *quality of life*. Review the use of hyphens to connect a group of words used together as an adjective. Next, look up The Economist Intelligence Unit's quality-of-life index on the Internet and answer the following questions: What factors are considered in determining a country's quality of life? Where does the U.S. rank on the index? Did the factors listed help you to understand the expression *quality of life*?

    As a group, think of another factor that should be added to the quality-of-life index and write a questionnaire or survey to measure that factor. Now join up with another group and answer each other's questionnaires. Each member of the group should respond individually to the other team's questionnaire. Keep track of the responses on paper or the blackboard. When you have finished, determine which group has the higher quality of life according to this factor.

20. **Analyze Policies** When it comes to most U.S. policies—agricultural policies, tax policies, spending policies—it is not always clear that they are accepted and implemented if benefits are greater than the costs. Tariffs and quotas are often scrutinized for efficiency. Research a current U.S. economic policy (aside from tariffs and quotas) and try to find articles that challenge the efficiency of a policy. Make a list of the pros and cons of your selected policy and then analyze whether you would consider the costs to outweigh the benefits of the policies or vice versa. Support your view with logical reasoning.

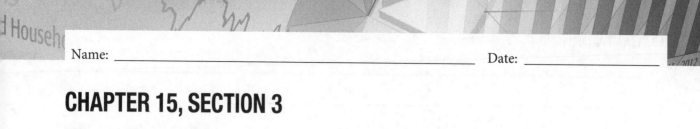

CHAPTER 15, SECTION 3
The Exchange Rate

To find out how much of your money you have to pay for a foreign good, you need to follow three steps:
1. Find the exchange rate.
2. Figure out how much of your money it takes to buy 1 unit of the foreign money.
3. Multiply the number of units in the price of the foreign good by your answer to step 2.

EXAMPLE
Assume that $1 = £0.87, and you want to find the dollar price of an item that costs £25.
Step 1: The exchange rate is $1 = £0.87.
Step 2: If $1 = £0.87, then £1 = $(1/0.87) = $1.15, rounded to the nearest cent.
Step 3: The price of the item in dollars is $1.15 × 25 = $28.75.

In questions 1 and 2, assume that the exchange rate is $1 × 25 Russian rubles.

1. How many dollars (rounded to the nearest cent) will it take to buy one ruble?

_____

2. Use your answer to question 1 to complete the following table.

	Price in rubles	Price in dollars
A Volga car	419,540	_____
A McDonald's Big Mac	160	_____
A souvenir coffee mug	430	_____
A picture book of Moscow	778	_____

In questions 3 and 4, assume that the exchange rate is 1 Swiss franc × $0.80.

3. How many Swiss francs (rounded to the nearest hundredth) will it take to buy one dollar?

_____

4. Use your answer to question 3 to complete the following table.

	Price in dollars	Price in francs
A Ford Focus car	17,000.00	_____
A McDonald's Big Mac	4.50	_____
A souvenir coffee mug	11.00	_____
A picture book of New York	19.00	_____

Imagine two countries, Narnia and Gondor. The people of Narnia use Narns as currency, and the people of Gondor use Gords as currency. The following table shows the exchange rates for Narns and Gords in two years. Use the information in the table to answer questions 5–10.

Year	Exchange rate
2015	1 Narn = 20 Gords
2016	1 Narn = 25 Gords

5. One Narn buys _____ in 2015.

6. One Narn buys _____ in 2016.

7. A Narn buys _____ Gords in 2016 than in 2015, so the Narn has

_____.

8. One Gord buys _____ in 2015.

9. One Gord buys _____ in 2016.

10. A Gord buys _____ Narns in 2016 than in 2015, so the Gord has

_____.

In each of the situations described in questions 11–14, determine whether you would prefer for the dollar to appreciate or depreciate relative to the euro.

11. You are planning a trip to France. _____

12. You are a U.S. businessperson whose chief competitor is a German company.

_____

13. Your factory relies on parts imported from Germany. _____

14. Your job depends on foreign tourists visiting the United States. _____

Apply what you have learned in this section by completing the following extension activity.

15. **Collaborate to Make a Choice** With a small group of classmates, imagine that you are planning a vacation in another country. You want to go where the dollar is strong; that is, where the exchange rate is in your favor. You are considering going to Japan, France, South Africa, or Mexico. Collaborate to research the current exchange rates in these countries and take notes about what you discover. Decide where to vacation based on where your dollar will go furthest. Research things you want to do and see in the country where you will be visiting and discuss the options with your group. As a group, decide on the details of your trip.

CHAPTER 15, SECTION 4

Economic Development

In questions 1–7, list the factors that some economists believe can aid growth and development and help poor countries prosper. Then briefly describe each factor.

1. *Factor:*

_____

Description:

_____

_____

_____

_____

2. *Factor:*

_____

Description:

_____

_____

_____

_____

3. *Factor:*

_____

Description:

_____

_____

_____

_____

4. *Factor:*

_____

Description:

_____

_____

_____

_____

5. *Factor:*

_____

Description:

_____

_____

_____

_____

6. *Factor:*

_____

Description:

_____

_____

_____

_____

7. *Factor:*

_____

Description:

_____

_____

_____

_____

Write your answer to question 8 on the lines provided.

8. Do international organizations exist that might be able to help less-developed countries? If so, identify these organizations and describe how they help these countries.

_____

_____

_____

_____

_____

_____

Apply what you have learned in this section by completing the following extension activities.

9. **Write a Narrative** Choose a less developed country and research it on the Internet or at the library. Find out what sorts of jobs people do there. Choose a job and find out about how much it pays, what it involves, and what the living conditions of a worker doing that job might be. Take notes about what you find. Write a narrative of a day in the life of a worker who does the job you researched. Start by describing the worker getting up in the morning and continue with them going to work, working, going home, and eating dinner. Include as many details as you can. Present your narrative to your class. As your classmates present their own narratives, take notes on the jobs and countries that they researched and compare them to your own narrative.

10. **Make Connections** Chapter 15 explained that free trade has a significant effect on a country's economic growth. Write an informative essay that analyzes how trade relates to growth and explains the connection in a way that would be understandable to a person who is unfamiliar with economic terms.

CHAPTER 16, SECTION 1

Stocks

Dividends

One reason people buy stocks is for the dividends they receive. If we divide the dividend (per share of stock) by the closing price (of the stock), we get the yield. The higher the yield of a stock, the better it is for the investor, all other things being the same.

Based on the above information and what you have learned about stocks, write your answers to questions 1–4 in the blanks provided.

1. What are dividends?

   _____

   _____

2. If you own 100 shares of company A and company A pays an annual dividend of $1.32 per share, how much would you receive in dividend payments for the year?

   _____

   _____

3. The dividend for a stock is listed as 1.43. What does this mean?

   _____

   _____

4. If the closing price of a stock is $53.48 and its dividend is $1.22, what is the yield?

   _____

Capital Gains and Losses

Another way people make money by investing in stock is by selling their stock for a price that is higher than their purchase price was. A **capital gain** is the amount of money made when stock is sold for a price that is higher than the purchase price. To calculate a capital gain, subtract the purchase price from the sale price and multiply that amount times the number of shares involved in the transactions.

Of course, stock does not always increase in value. A **capital loss** is the amount of money lost when stock is sold for a price that is lower than the purchase price. To calculate a capital loss, subtract the sale price from the purchase price and multiply that amount times the number of shares involved in the transactions.

The entries in the following table appeared in the stock market page of a newspaper on Friday, October 14. Use the table to answer questions 5–15.

52W high	52W low	Stock	Ticker	Div	Yield %	P/E	Vol 00s	High	Low	Close	Net chg
53.17	31.93	BestBuy	BBY	0.32	0.73	20	47579	43.43	42.17	43.29	+0.79
321.28	133.40	Google	GOOG			86	84991	300.23	292.54	296.14	−1.30
46.99	41.51	Kellogg	K	1.11	2.42	20	9769	45.96	45.25	45.82	+0.23
27.94	23.82	Microsoft	MSFT	0.32	1.29	22	532632	24.73	24.48	24.67	+0.08
59.39	49.82	Pepsico	PEP	1.04	1.81	25	33994	57.85	57.18	57.51	+0.26
9.43	3.45	SiriusXM	SIRI				606526	6.53	5.82	6.17	−0.25
57.89	42.33	WalMart	WMT	0.60	1.33	18	117735	45.26	44.60	45.04	+0.28

5. Which stock has the highest yield?

_____

6. If you bought 100 shares of Sirius XM Radio Inc. at the highest price for the year and sold it at the lowest price for the year, what was your capital loss? Explain.

_____

_____

7. If you bought 100 shares of Best Buy at the lowest price for the year and sold it at the closing price on October 14, what was your capital gain? Explain.

_____

_____

8. If you bought 100 shares of Google at the lowest price for the year and sold it at the highest price for the year, what was your capital gain? Explain.

_____

_____

9. How many shares of Microsoft traded on Friday, October 14?

_____

_____

10. What was the closing price of Pepsico on Thursday, October 13?

_____

_____

11. If you have owned 100 shares of Kellogg for a year, how much money did you receive in dividend payments last year?

_____

_____

12. If you owned 200 shares of Wal-Mart, how much would you expect to receive in dividend payments this year?

_____

_____

PE Ratio

The PE ratio is obtained by dividing the closing price per share (of stock) by the net earnings per share. If a stock has a PE ratio of, say, 20, this means that the stock is selling for a share price that is 20 times its earnings per share. Write your answers to questions 13–16 in the blanks provided.

13. What might you conclude about Sirius XM, which has a closing price but does not have a PE ratio?

_____

_____

14. What is Wal-Mart's PE ratio and what does it mean?

_____

_____

15. What does Google's relatively high PE ratio signify?

_____

_____

_____

16. Why are people willing to buy a stock with a high PE ratio?

_____

_____

_____

Apply what you have learned in this section by completing the following extension activities.

17. **Present Financial News** Research recent IPOs (initial public offerings) on the Internet. Choose one IPO and find out how much the stock sold for, how well it sold, and how it has performed since. Next, research the reasons behind these facts. Why did the people who purchased the stock believe it was valuable? What happened after the IPO to make the stock perform well or poorly?

    Deliver a presentation to your class about the IPO you researched, telling how the stock performed and the reasons behind it. Use accessible language in addition to relevant vocabulary words you encountered in your research or in your textbook. When you have finished, take and respond to questions from your teacher and classmates.

18. **Write a Translation** View a video of a TV news stock market report. Pause the video as needed to review your understanding or to replay any segment that you did not understand. Using Exhibit 16-3 in your book, which lists expressions commonly used in financial reports, write a translation of the report using accessible language. You will probably need to view the report multiple times to complete your translation. As you are working, make a list of the terms and expressions that you did not immediately understand and note their definitions for future reference.

19. **Collaborate to Research Stock Performance** In a small group, collaborate to make a list of everything you know about the stock market. Next, come up with three companies whose products you buy and then research the performance of those companies' stocks over the previous year. You should read articles and view graphic organizers or other visuals to maximize your understanding. Figure out how much you would have gained or lost if you had bought a single share of each company's stock on January 1 of last year and sold it on January 1 of this year, and create or locate graphs for each company to show how the stock's value changed over time. Based on your findings, decide which company would have been the best investment for that duration of time.

CHAPTER 16, SECTION 2

Bonds

A bond is another type of investment. Write your answers to questions 1 and 2 in the blanks provided.

1. What are the three ways a company can raise money?

   _____

   _____

2. What is a bond?

   _____

   _____

In questions 3–5, list the components of a bond. Then describe each component.

3. *Component:*

   _____

   Description:

   _____

   _____

4. *Component:*

   _____

   Description:

   _____

   _____

5. *Component:*

   _____

   Description:

   _____

   _____

Elena pays $10,000 for a bond with a face value of $10,000 and a coupon rate of 6 percent. Scott buys a bond for $9,500. The face value of the bond is $10,000 and the coupon rate is 6 percent. Fill in the blanks in questions 6–14 with the correct answers.

6. Elena will receive a coupon payment of _____ each year.

7. When the bond matures, Elena will receive _____ from the issuer of the bond.

8. The yield that Elena will receive on the bond is _____.

9. If the maturity date is five years from the day Elena buys the bond, she will earn a total of _____ on her investment.

10. Scott will receive a coupon payment of _____ each year.

11. The yield that Scott will receive on the bond is _____.

12. When the bond matures, Scott will receive _____ from the issuer of the bond.

13. If the maturity date is five years from the day Scott buys the bond, he will earn a total of _____ on his investment.

14. Both Elena and Scott bought bonds with face values of $10,000, coupon rates of 6 percent, and maturity dates five years from the date of purchase. Scott will earn _____ on his investment than Elena will earn on her investment because he paid _____ than the face value of the bond.

Write your answers to questions 15–20 in the blanks provided.

15. What is the main difference among corporate bonds, municipal bonds, and treasury bills?

    _____

    _____

    _____

16. Which type of investment, stocks or bonds, is riskier? Why?

    _____

    _____

    _____

17. What is the relationship between the returns and the risks of various investments?

    _____

    _____

18. If a person wants high returns from investments and is willing to take high risks, he or she would likely invest mainly in _____.

Applying the Principles Workbook

19. If a person wants low risk investing, she or he would likely invest mainly in

_____.

20. If the yield on a 10-year Treasury bond is 4.60 percent and the yield on a 10-year corporate bond is 5.26 percent, which bond do you think would involve more risk? Why?

_____

_____

_____

Investing in the Future

The Your Personal Economics feature in Chapter 16 discusses how a person can invest in their future by utilizing retirement plans and accounts. It also discusses the ways in which people can invest in their community through charitable giving.

Charitable giving is not limited to a donation of time and money. You can also donate personal property, such as vehicles and clothing. This method of donation benefits you by conveniently disposing of property you no longer want (organizations often pick up donations) and may entitle you to a charitable tax deduction. Most organizations will resell your property and use the resulting income to support their organization. The costs of disposing of your personal property in this manner include any loss of use as well as the opportunity cost of the income you would receive if you sold the property yourself.

Apply what you have learned in this section by completing the following extension activity.

21. **Research Donation Opportunities** Using the Internet, research a charitable organization in your community that accepts motor vehicle donations. Find out how the donation will be used and in an informative essay, analyze the cost and benefits of donating a vehicle to the organization you chose. Include costs and benefits to both the person donating the vehicle and the organization that receives the vehicle. Support your analysis with logical reasoning.

CHAPTER 16, SECTION 3

Futures and Options

Futures Contracts

Different people have different tolerances for risk. Some people are willing to assume high risk and other people look for ways to insure against risk. Write your answers to questions 1–6 in the blanks provided.

1. What is a futures contract?

   _____
   _____
   _____

2. Why might Daphne, who uses a particular commodity in the production of her good, enter into a futures contract?

   _____
   _____
   _____

3. Why would Stephanie enter into a futures contract with Daphne?

   _____
   _____
   _____
   _____

4. Why might Michael, who provides a commodity, enter into a futures contract?

   _____
   _____
   _____

5. Why would Stephanie, the speculator from question 3, enter into a futures contract with Michael?

   _____
   _____
   _____

6. How can a futures contract help reduce risk?

_____

_____

Call and Put Options

Using options is a way to make money in the stock market without actually investing in stocks. It also allows a person to avoid some risk in investing. Write your answers to questions 7–13 in the blanks provided.

7. What is a call option?

_____

_____

8. How does the buyer of a call option profit?

_____

_____

_____

9. What is a put option?

_____

_____

_____

10. How does the buyer of a put option profit?

_____

_____

_____

11. If you think the price of a certain stock is going to fall in the next few months, what kind of option would you buy? Why?

_____

_____

12. If you think the price of a certain stock is going to rise in the next few months, what kind of option would you buy? Why?

_____

_____

13. How could stock options as a form of compensation be used as an incentive to employees to be productive workers?

_____

_____

_____

_____

_____

Apply what you have learned in this section by completing the following extension activities.

14. **Make Connections** Recall that in Chapter 3 you learned about the various characteristics of a free enterprise system. In an informative essay, explain how the investment opportunities available in a free enterprise system such as (i) starting your own business, (ii) buying stocks, and (iii) buying bonds are a benefit of the U.S. free enterprise system. Support your work with examples and logical reasoning.

15. **Hold a Small-Group Discussion** In a small group, research and discuss the benefits of the free economic system, particularly the creation of wealth and how stocks and bonds are part of this system. Be sure to explain the difference between stocks and bonds and describe why businesses sell stocks and bonds. Then describe how investing in these financial instruments helps investors build wealth. Use what you have learned in this chapter as a guide to research and prepare for the discussion. Take turns identifying how the free enterprise system supports the creation of wealth and support your statements with specific examples and logical reasoning.